RABIES

CW00377004

HOLY CANCER

HOLY CANCER

How A Cow Saved My Life

AMIT VAIDYA

HEALING VAIDYA &
ADITYA PRAKASHAN
New Delhi

First published, 2015

ISBN 978-81-7742-147-7

Published by Healing Vaidya & Aditya Prakashan,
2/18, Ansari Road, New Delhi – 110 002.

email: contact@adityaprakashan.com
website: www.adityaprakashan.com

Printed at Thomson Press (India) Ltd.

This book is my attempt to share my truth to the best ability of my memory. Some names, locations, dialogues and identifying details have been changed to respect the privacy of the people involved.

To cancer.
You've been there even when no one else was.
And you're still with me even when I have everything.
Thank you for giving me a legacy.

Contents

Acknowledgements

A story about living just wouldn't be possible without the rest of the world contributing. I would like to thank every single person who has featured in my life, in any and every light.

We are the sum of our experiences and while I could wish that things were different—I have accepted it and realized that my life and this moment would not have been possible had even one thing gone differently.

The two people most responsible for my ability to survive and to live in happiness are my parents. Dad was my biggest advocate and his unconditional support is still something that echoes in my ear when I need it most. Even more than a decade later, his selfless love for me is stronger than anyone in my life. On the other hand, Mom was simply the greatest friend I could have had. Her ability to share, give and put other's needs ahead of hers, I try my best to live by that example. But her greatest gift to me was the lesson she shared with me towards the end of her life—that no matter what adversity we face in life, end the day living it to the fullest, going to sleep at night thankful for that day and literally being at peace if that were to be the last day of my life.

In all my travels I've met such extraordinary people and to name them all would be next to impossible. I've also lost so many amazing souls along this shared journey and I dedicate this book to all of them.

Melixa: My sister, my friend, my cancer soulmate. I miss you and I shine a little brighter because of your undying love and optimism.

Mahima: I tried to help you and I'm sorry that as your brother, I failed you. You deserved a much longer life and I hope you forgive me for not pushing you more.

Ravi: I saw myself in you. I so wish I could have taken your place, as your family's neverending support was like I was watching a home movie. I'm still not sure I understand why, but you reminded me that despite what I didn't have, I was still very lucky.

Flavia: Life isn't as serious as we make it out to be and you taught me that even in the height of pain, finding a way to laugh always made things a little bit easier.

Ansuya Massi: Even in such a short time, you were more of a mother to me than the many women who should have filled Mom's shoes, at least partially... thank you.

Bill: The greatest gift you gave me was an amazing friend in Peggy. I feel so lucky to have someone who knows and understands my journey like no other.

Melinda: Sometimes seeing you and Karl together reminded me of my parents but to imagine both of you fighting the same disease simultaneously, it's a cruel and sometimes senseless world. Your kindness and loving nature lives on in Christy and I'm truly grateful to have her in my life.

Harry: You were the rock of your family and your family was there for me in my darkest hour. It is your character and humanity that housed me good fortune at a point in time when I was feeling most alone.

Jean: Every time I dare even ask the question why, I think of you. You were God's gift in that you led your life with positivity and despite what transpired you shed that light with whomever you came in contact.

Vinay: I was meant to be there with you and your family at the end. I feel very honoured that you gave me your blessings for this book.

Bapuji: I never had the privilege of meeting you Bapuji but throughout my life I was compared to you many many times... of course minus the cigarette habit. While we know what caused your cancer, you became the trailblazer for the disease in our family and I'm proud to be your grandson and to carry that label as well.

Ba: your age was mostly responsible for the cancer but I'm still thankful that you were there for me. No one should have to suffer the loss of a child and I know how broken you'd become after Dad died. You consoled Mom when I got sick and I'm so grateful that despite whatever health issues, you best exemplified that life goes on.

I'd like to thank the hundreds of doctors, nurses, aides and support staff around the world at this point who made each hospital feel like a second home (and sometimes first home!) for me. Singling anyone out feels like any one component is more important than the other but the truth is that without any one of you—my story would not be the same.

With that said, my list of friends, relations, strangers and spirits who've met me on this journey in my life, the list could go on endlessly and continue to expand with each given day. I'm incredibly grateful to have had so many who stood by me at any given moment in time. As we continue to live, our lives will perhaps intersect again enabling me room for my thankfulness to grow and evolve.

To my editor, Shalini, thank you for getting into my head and stylizing me into—making sense.

I'm truly appreciative of everything that has come my way and know even when I stand alone—I am standing high because of the support of all of you.

Prologue

This is a story about positivity, overcoming obstacles and finding peace and happiness in life—no matter what. Because of that, I have deliberately attempted to refrain from focusing on the negative aspects of my journey. This book could be dedicated entirely to those who didn't provide support, who didn't offer help, who said no when I needed them to say yes, the emotional toll it took on me and how much more challenging they made my life but instead I'd like to acknowledge those that were there for me.

From the relatives to the friends to the strangers who became friends and then turned into family, I have been incredibly lucky to have such wonderful people in my life. They have taught me to let go of expectations because when you don't expect, life throws you special surprises in the best kind of way.

I feel privileged to have had the luxury of meeting new souls along the way to compensate for the absences I felt in my life whether they were by my choice or theirs.

If there is one thing I know in the last ten years that I did right—it was that I always put my health first. Everything, I mean everything, was second to that. Many disagreed with my priorities; I lost a lot of support along my journey because of this. When your priority is money or work or appearance within society, it's a different story and a completely different journey.

I don't have the right to judge others, but it pains me that as a society we judge those who are fighting such challenging battles and expect them to not only beat whatever battle quickly but also assimilate back into society, without acknowledging the changes that have occurred both internally and externally.

It has been a long and winding road and I'm happy that the journey continues... and the volumes of my life keep adding.

With that said, this is not a how-to-cure book nor is it a blank endorsement to any particular form or type of treatment out there. This book attempts to chronicle and highlight my individual road. It is my intent and my goal to open options and opportunities on exploring other possibilities for healing. Knowledge is what gives us choice and I hope this starts a dialogue of self-discovery for others—more so a guide and not a playbook.

CHAPTER 1

Fight Or Flight

More than a drug is what I need
Need a change of scenery
Need a new life
['Say Something' by James]

People get a second chance if they are lucky, but getting a second life—that's another story. When I was twenty-three, I went to see a palm reader at a county fair in New York, she very boldly stated that my lifeline had an abrupt end and that it was sooner than I would have ever expected. I shrugged it off of course, determined never to see a palm reader again, so as to not hear such morbid predictions.

Yet after losing your father unexpectedly in your mid-twenties; being diagnosed with cancer yourself just two years later; going into remission after three years of treatment only to become caregiver to your mother, who fought an even more aggressive form and type of cancer till she died—and then to find out your cancer had returned and metastasized—you wonder if the palm reader had foreseen correctly. Yet here I was, still alive and kicking. There is no other explanation—this is my second life.

When and where did this new life begin? I'd like to believe it happened midway inflight between leaving America and arriving in India. It had been eight long years since I had visited. It was the widest gap my passport had ever seen. So much had transpired between the last entry stamp and this one. Yet I was feeling a sense of déjà vu. The last trip I made to India was after my father's death. This time I was traveling after my mother's. Of course, this was also likely to be my final journey there or anywhere for that matter.

It was just two days prior to my trip. I still remember sitting under the white light as my doctor looked at me. He simply couldn't muster the words he had so professionally written in a letter I was to travel with, in case of an emergency—'six months' to live. While no one can predict (perhaps, except that palm reader many years ago) when we are going to die, I had gained confidence over the years in the medical community's ability to make somewhat accurate time frame estimates.

They had given Mom 'one to two years'. Her tests indicated she'd likely last longer, but her tumours were aggressive and despite countless chemotherapies, radiation treatments and even a clinical trial—she lasted fourteen months. It was actually quite impressive given her unbelievable series of challenges.

We had both learnt to accept whatever came our way over time, starting with the unexpected death of my father in February 2004, as a result of fatal complications during a routine bypass surgery. As he was rolled away for the procedure, he kissed Mom and told her he'd see her again shortly. She was left waiting.

Understanding how everything can be uprooted in a moment and that too, with eyes wide open, changed the two of us. This got further tested when I was first diagnosed with stage one gastric adenocarcinoma, only two years later in the summer of 2006. The years have now blended together like a bad memory of chemotherapy cycles, blood tests, scans, and countless side effects and complications.

Just when we thought that I might have possibly won my battle, Mom had the baton passed on to her, diagnosed with a stage three anaplastic oligodendroglioma. I look back and wonder if my remission was nothing more than a karmic pause that enabled Mom to have the support she needed for her final days.

Malignant brain cancer is unlike any other form of the disease. It affects every part of you. Having been Mom's sole caregiver throughout her battle, I had seen the good, the bad and the wish-on-not-even-your-worst-enemy. What let me sleep peacefully at night, post her death, was comfort in knowing that I had done everything possible to ensure the highest quality of life for her, each and every day during that journey.

Now here I was, an orphan at the age of thirty three, on what was very possibly my final plane ride, back to a home country that felt foreign to me. I re-read the letter that my doctor had written. The 'six month' time frame seemed to jump out and I wondered what would become of my remaining days. It was just over a year since Mom's death in early 2011 and realizing that in spite of countless chemotherapy sessions, more radiation and yet another clinical trial over the year, nothing was working. I knew it was time to stop trying the same thing and to perhaps make a radical change.

For years my extended family and relatives had been insisting that Mom and I get on a flight and come to India. While nothing would have made us happier, the reality was that our lives were not that easily transferrable. Between Mom's illness and being in an unfamiliar place, I was not sure I could be the best caregiver or medical advocate that she needed, given her routine and her growing disabilities.

At this point I was kidding myself thinking that I did not need some love and affection. The consoling by an elder can minimize any level of stress, no matter when. I had spent the last year so thankful for my friends, who hadn't let me stay one night alone. Still, we sometimes want what we can't have. I have spent years of my life hoping that I'd recover. Hope is something you must hold onto because without it, you are that much closer to giving it all up.

Yet, with hope we sometimes cloud ourselves of the reality that surrounds us. My father always preached health before wealth and I chose to follow those words after my initial diagnosis. At a point in time when I should have been focusing my attention on climbing up the professional ladder, I chose to fight the more important battle of my life. With Mom's encouragement and support, I stopped my full time work, focusing solely on my expected 'return to normalcy'. If I let my career interfere with my recovery, would it be worth it?

The journey went on far longer than anticipated. So many unexpected twists and turns narrated the story, that both Mom and I lost grip of a budding reality—that the family and friends who had supported us emotionally and eventually financially were expecting closure, sooner rather than later.

The biggest lie I told myself was that I was going to get better soon, repay all the favours and debts that Mom and I had acquired as a result of my health and finish the pending works that had been accumulating over the course of my treatment.

Slowly the phone calls, the inquiries, the concern all faded and judgments, misconceptions and misbelief clouded these relationships. Those we were closest to ended up adding to our stress rather than alleviating it. There was no bad blood, but there was silence. When fighting an illness, sometimes silence is the worst possible poison, because it comes across as apathy. When you are trying so hard and no one cares to express that they wish to see you survive—it's worse than any cancer.

For years I saw that poison slowly but surely affect Mom. I can't say that it was responsible for her cancer but it certainly did not help. While I knew I had done everything possible, I couldn't control the indifference. I wasn't going to let 'them' win and I wasn't going to let that tarnish the memory and legacy of Mom.

With the news that my cancer had now metastasized and I was fighting a cancer diagnosis now spreading from my stomach to my lungs, my liver and my spine—it seemed that my time would come to an end very soon.

My friends rallied and tried to be there as best as they could, but a mounting feeling that I was preparing for my death overtook me. A reckless and careless behavioural pattern began. Maybe it was a permanent state of 'chemo-brain' but my cloudy judgments were affecting my daily reality. The frustration of not having a full-time permanent caregiver like Mom, who was there for me the first time around, her absence and then the acknowledgement of her death became just too much for me to handle.

I tried my best to find substitutes and transfer my feelings to others who wanted to be there for me. However at the end of the day, understanding that everyone returned to their respective families and I was again an outsider and that too all alone, became the toughest non-chemo pill to swallow.

I had been in touch with relatives in India, on and off, but frankly only to a limited extent. Filling them in on my declining health seemed too daunting. The first time around Mom had been the primary chain of communication. This time, it was up to me. When I could barely engage with those around me, speaking to distant relatives was just too much of a challenge.

Thankfully, writing had always been a refuge for me, a place to express my thoughts, my reality and also share my fears and insecurities. As my treatments continued and I found myself without the support I needed—I had to reach out to my relatives. My one cousin Gautum took a particular interest in me.

Just as candidly as I had expressed my concerns and struggles, he expressed his wish to help and his desire for me to come to India, where I could perhaps have other treatment options and the mental and financial relief I had been seeking for quite a long time.

The seed was planted in my head but I didn't want to accept that possibility. I had too many obstacles in my life to make the trip to India. From physical disabilities (my right arm and hand were weakened as a result of excessive neuropathy), to having to leave my work (and perhaps jeopardizing my health insurance), to finally leaving my comfort zone of known doctors and hospitals—I was concerned.

When I looked at the present situation and my debilitating health, I had to consider the reality of shifting to a nursing home where I'd have care, if needed. It's a daunting task to be in your thirty's alone sans family and shopping for your own palliative care. No choice is easy, but perhaps, I was blessed to have the strength to make plans for myself and ensure that I got to live the rest of my life as I deserved—however short or long that was going to be.

Silver linings sometimes appear without any anticipation. Having stopped all my allopathic treatments, except for a trial drug that I was committed to continuing (basically for life), I had begun to explore alternative treatments. I had been reading about certain herbs and naturopathic treatments that were shown to help in the quality of life for cancer patients.

I never truly believed that non-traditional medicines had curative qualities other than alleviating a side effect or overall improving one's health. My father was a chemist who spent his entire life working in the pharmaceutical industry, contributing to the actual development of life-saving drugs. He was a doctor at heart, so his faith and belief in the allopathic world was so strong—it was as if there were no doubts in his mind.

What's interesting though was that he was an avid reader and researcher. Wherever he'd find a health tip, he'd cut out the excerpt, do further investigation and if it had value for anyone, he'd voice his recommendation about the benefits of such and such pill and/or treatment. Perhaps because his death was so nonsensical for me, I began to question everything about Dad.

He was a wise man no doubt, but his trust in pills doing the trick without much of our own involvement in the process, felt like a lazy answer. He would evaluate his diet but do little to change it, lecture me about exercise yet do the bare minimum and seldom explore natural remedies for our health.

Like Dad, once I was diagnosed, I made an active choice to research, study and examine any and all articles pertaining to my disease. I freely spoke about my illness, my anxieties and my willingness to try anything. It is

7

for this reason that perhaps despite my early stage and initial diagnosis—I modified my diet overnight. I tried to exercise but my compromised immunity and specific tumour location often caused strain.

As my metastasis continued, I became all the more aware of the need to find alternative treatments to help me cope with the mounting side effects that were seriously affecting the quality of my day-to-day life. My research and my friend's persistent recommendations had me explore some Chinese medicine and Ayurveda.

One such effective complimentary treatment was acupuncture that I took along side my chemoradiation. Despite so many of my fellow patient friends facing complications from diarrhoea to excess fatigue to weight loss, it seemed I was shielded from the many side effects of my cocktail chemo selection.

The endless steroids that had become so commonplace in my system were going to have some traditional antidotes, in an attempt to reverse some of my physical ailments. By the time I read my doctor's letter, I was already two months into having incorporated some supplements into my routine. I knew about tulsi and neem, but these were pills that I knew had gone through some levels of processing and had made the long journey from some remote farmland in India to a natural store here in Manhattan, many months later.

I didn't expect much from the pills, yet there was an almost immediate effect. The extensive neuropathy I had experienced, from far too many rounds of chemo, had begun to affect my ability to hold items in my right hand. Seeing my hand slowly regain its ability, gave me the courage to pursue a dialogue once again with Gautum about a potential visit to India.

I knew before traveling so far I'd need to do a test flight. For countless years my blood count levels or some relating number, was either too high or too low, so the doctors always added the disclaimer about the risks of flying, traveling and overexerting myself.

One of our dear friends Paulina, who had also lost her husband to cancer some time back, had kindly stepped in and been a motherly support to me. She invited me down to her home in West Palm Beach, Florida. As a former nurse and caregiver, I knew this would be a safe trip for me.

I took all the energy and strength I had and made that first trip. After being trapped in New York for almost seven years, as it seemed, I was finally leaving my home and reaching another part of the Atlantic Ocean—a part where I hadn't spread the ashes of both my parents.

The trip was the most liberating and exhilarating I had felt in an unimaginable amount of time. Not to have every street, every shop, every restaurant, every building have a history, have a meaning—to see a new place after so many years—I felt like I was living another life.

The walk along the ocean gave me a sense of comfort and a feeling of great fortune. I was able to break away, something my mother had not been able to do from the first minute of my diagnosis. I stood barefoot in the sand and reflected on everything that had transpired till that moment. It was just a split second realization but at that moment I knew that I'd be okay. I felt ready to accept the inevitable.

I flew back and spoke to my Doctor about the possibility of flying to India. Happy to see my spirits lifted significantly after my trip down South, he didn't see the travels being an issue. I'd have to be cautious and fly with medical directions but a short two to three week trip would not be a problem.

Within twenty four hours, I had the letter in my hand and had already spoken to Gautum and his parents (Vinod *Mama* & Saroj *Mami*). They were elated with my decision and immediately booked my ticket for me. They suggested that I stay longer but I was concerned as my medication schedule was once every three weeks and with one specific experimental drug unavailable in India—I needed to be cautious.

Even with a round trip fare booked, I must be honest, there was part of me that was of the mind-set that perhaps I shall not return. In my mind, I had this cinematic vision of my final days. Making the journey across the world would be this poetic statement. I made it to India—making the trip Mom was unable to—providing a sense of closure for my relatives (namely her brothers and sisters); returning back to my ancestral roots; closing my eyes in the birthplace of my parents who ironically had both passed away in my home country. All these thoughts circled my mind and made me surreally optimistic about my limited future.

My childhood friend Adrienne had been such an amazing support to me since Mom had passed away. I had always seen her strong and composed but there was something different as we hugged and she saw me off at the airport. Neither of us said it, but it felt like there was finality to the goodbye. We didn't know if I'd make it back and if so, in what condition. There was hope and excitement for the trip that lay ahead, but as I saw her drive off, I wondered what was to come.

While waiting in the check-in line, I flashbacked to the last time I flew to India. I was mourning the loss of my father and accompanying my grieving mother as we went to visit all our family. Now, eight years later on March 18, 2012 I was making my next trip, this time I was mourning the loss of my mother and off to do the same. I wasn't sure if after meeting everyone I'd ever see them again. As it turns out, that did become the case—but for a very different reason.

CHAPTER 2

Honeymoon In Hindustan

Just hold on we're going home
Just hold on we're going home
It's hard to do these things alone
Just hold on we're going home (home)
['Hold On We're Going Home' by Drake]

It's a strange feeling to land somewhere and to feel this connection, then realize that the link that associated you to that place is no longer there with you, but rather only there inside of you. This trip to India felt much less like a homecoming, mainly because for me, my home was where my parents were and sadly they were no longer physically present anywhere in the world.

As foolish as it sounds though, upon landing at the airport a naïve perhaps wishful part of me, somewhere deep down, hoped all the years that had passed were perhaps part of some sick experiment; that my parents were actually in some bubble and were living in India all this time and would be picking me up at the airport.

Of course for that to be true, I'd have to erase the vivid memories that came with me to India. Saying goodbye and then pressing the electric button for both their cremations in the United States were two images forever ensconced in me.

In life we are gifted with two people who, if lucky, selflessly advocate for us—no matter what. In my case, both my parents had offered that level of blessing and protection. But after their early deaths, it seemed next to impossible to find anyone even remotely close who would offer me any kind of assurance, love and frankly stability. That security blanket had been pulled from under my feet in the early morning hours of January 5, 2011 on the day of my mother's death.

Perhaps my life had prepared me for this reality. I have always had an overabundance of people who actually chose to want to be there, rather than those who in some form or another felt a kind of obligation and actually refrained from connecting with me at all.

Thankfully my good family friends, the Shahs, came to pick me up and I was whisked away to their farmhouse, a somewhat reclusive space tucked on the outskirts of Delhi. Seeing them and being with them—felt surreal. I had seen them just a few months back in New York. They were actually a huge inspiration to me and in my decision to make this journey to India. After years and years of hearing that I needed to make a trip to see everyone, that it would be good for me to offer family and friends the opportunity to be there and to take care of me in this time of need, it was a welcome and comforting change.

It's a strange thing to realize, that the extended family I saw my parents spend their entire lives longing for; going out of their way to make sure they succeeded and lived happily, develop complete apathy post their deaths and when coming to meet me as a patient.

Don't get me wrong—there was a lovely honeymoon phase. I came to India and literally every cousin, every relative I had, came out of the wood works to see me and to see how I was doing. To say I have a big family would be an understatement. Dad had two brothers and seven sisters.

Mom had three brothers and five sisters. I had no grandparents and adding up the tally of both sides of the family, I had forty-one first cousins of which over thirty-one were married and twenty-nine had children. We used to visit India regularly when I was a kid and I had even lived in New Delhi for a few years during middle and high school, so while we weren't in their lives actively on a daily basis, I was a known and loved member of the family. However, something had changed. The visits to see me were coming from a point of responsibility and a sense of obligation. Families may not believe in competition, but they certainly were not going to publicly look like the insensitive ones, by not visiting the mourning relative who also happened to be sick.

Illness is a private matter. Every patient should be entitled to a level of privacy that enables them to make proper decisions as they deem fit. However, in India I quickly discovered this doesn't exist. People show concern by wanting to know every specific medical detail whether they understand one word of a medical report or not.

In my life if there is one thing I've learnt, after watching my parents (more specifically Dad) make the same mistake again and again, is to not over share information with people who have absolutely no intention of doing anything with it.

All my relatives showed concern and wanted to 'know exactly what's wrong with me'. Yet fully aware that I was alone, without parents and unsure of my financial status, they were afraid to take on any level of responsibility until having had all these pertinent pieces of information. They hesitated from actually becoming an advocate or volunteering as a caregiver.

It's understandable as everybody has a life story. The years that had passed had created a sense of mystery around my life. This developed into a cloud of doubt in their minds, which even my physical presence could not counter. While other patients lost weight, I gained. I arrived at Delhi Airport weighing 102 kgs (down slightly from the 107 kgs I had reached post radiation that previous summer).

Thinking I was just fat and bloated, they didn't realize that I had been on steroids for almost five years. Since I did not have surgery, the toxins from the endless rounds of chemotherapy and radiation had actually built up in my system. I wasn't able to exercise properly or eat certain foods for long stretches of time—these were obstacles to my health.

Rather than try to understand or even ask questions, the knee-jerk response of indifference took precedence. Upon seeing this I knew that ignorance was not going to change to advocacy—no matter what I hoped.

Still my grief over the loss of my parents was shared, albeit temporarily. While clearly they didn't share the same intensity of grief, my aunts and uncles were a link to those stories, to the past and to a part of myself I thought I had lost. In my very adult life, to once again be transformed to my childhood and to feel that level of comfort was something that made my three-week trip to India so fulfilling.

It was a joyous reunion across two big cities and two sides of families. While I may have been the main reason behind the gatherings, it was equally a chance for the already close relatives to get together, meet and catch up. I spent time with everyone but it was at a very superficial level, all jokes and smiles. Perhaps because of that, everything appeared brighter than the reality. In short meetings, it's very challenging to discuss anything serious in nature or unload and share any feelings.

Still, there was a lovely moment of quiet contemplation on one breakfast morning in Mumbai, where two of Mom's sisters (Sapna *Massi* & Pooja *Massi*), asked me about how her final days were spent. It felt like the trip I had wanted was happening as I shared stories about their beautiful sister. It was then that Pooja Massi rather non chalantly talked about the benefit of alternative therapies and questioned what if Mom had gone that route? She suggested I try something she had read about in a Gujarati health magazine.

She happened to have a copy of that publication and began to read out this article about a Cancer Hospital that claimed to cure cancer through Ayurveda and 'cowpathy' for one rupee. The hospital was situated in Sevak, Gujarat and the treatment course lasted eleven days. It went on in some detail about what the treatment course involved, it included the use of the Indian cow for portions of the therapy. We debated the legitimacy of the claims as the process seemed so out of the box. I couldn't read the article as it was in Gujarati, but I did say I'd look up the treatment online and see if there was any merit to the claims. This spring boarded into a chat about traditional medicine and both massis shared stories of people they knew who had benefited from Ayurveda, not necessarily for cancer but for a variety of lifestyle diseases.

All of us knew there were limitations to 'alternative medicine'. However I had become an open-minded sceptic having seen first-hand that by simply incorporating certain herbs and pills into my routine, I had significantly reversed the challenges I was facing. From my neuropathic-related side effects to a clearer frame of mind—I couldn't discount an option too easily.

It was a minor moment but it had a major impact on me. To have such a frank discussion about health, choices and ultimately my illness and the one that also took Mom's life—it was a breakfast that fuelled me more than anything had in months.

The emotional refill that I received quickly became addictive. The years I had spent away from extended family felt foolish. Those lonely days and nights that I had simply accepted as my reality became inexcusable, as I felt a bevy of support at my disposal.

My elder relatives praised me for the care I had given to my mother at her most challenging moments. I could see the love that the siblings and cousins had for one another. Yet as I visited each home, I also saw that the time away had caught up with them as well. No longer were my aunts and uncles the primary forces in their respective families. Just as I had had to step up and become the caregiver to Mom, I saw in house after house that my cousins had also stepped up and become the leaders of their families.

But there were some stark differences. For them this was a responsibility, something that sons (and in certain homes daughters) were obligated to fulfil. Of course the decision to do so was rooted in love, but as part of a traditional Indian society there are certain pre-set guidelines and whether they wanted to or not my cousins had to adhere to these standards and not just them, but their respective spouses and subsequently their children.

It's a tall order but joint families still reign supreme and within minutes, I was able to work out the power dynamics of each home. Despite the closeness (whether genuinely there or perhaps my wishful thinking from childhood), I quickly realized that I was a welcome guest but I was also a guest with a pre-set expiration date, as I had a return date back to my life in America.

As my date to fly back approached, I began to wonder if perhaps, staying a bit longer would prove that much more healing as the preceding days had been.

I had returned back to the Shahs' farmhouse in Delhi. While there, they had made it clear that whenever I visited, I could use their house as my base. I appreciated this as any space that was welcoming and filled with love felt like home to me.

While staying there, I had been introduced to my family friend's yoga teacher, *Guruji* as their daughter Kaira called him. A former gangster turned yoga master, he came daily to the house. When we met, he gave me suggestions on alleviating some of the pain I was having and also some meditative and yogic techniques that would improve my blood circulation, physical stamina and overall health. I was open to his suggestions but my limits were many. He spoke to me about some more radical practices, but I was sceptical about them mainly because I knew, that in reality I didn't actually have the time to try them out.

Time flew so fast, three weeks went by overnight. As the hello hugs turned to goodbye kisses, my heart sank a little further. I was never one to host a pity party for myself but there was a cruel irony in the fact that I had come 7300 miles to bid farewell and return back to my 'home', a facility where the end of my days would be shared with the elderly, sickly and strangers. It was something I was thankful that, neither of my parents had to see.

It wasn't easy in the case of my mother, but there was literally no moment in her entire illness that she was without my support. I was there one hundred percent physically, mentally, and emotionally. Perhaps my nerves, coupled with the positive energy everyone had been channelling towards me on this trip seemed to stop me in my tracks.

As prepared as I was to die and as much peace as I had made with keeping a distance and not getting anyone attached to me or getting attached to anyone more than I already was—it was a harsh reality I was facing. I hadn't found solace but I did find life and a will to live. I began to question why I had even made this journey. Was I just being cruel to myself, giving myself these happy memories for a short while before going back to close my eyes in solitude?

However, I also knew the reality. Without sharing my medical details and not allowing my relatives to take a more active role in my decision-making process, I was also robbing them of the opportunity to truly become my caregivers. At the same time, I did not want their involvement, as I felt that there was nothing left for me to try.

Additionally, I was well aware of the limited capacities of my elder relatives. With the change of guard in each family, my fate was sealed. While there was love, there wasn't room for that love in their lives. As I had seen in the US with my few relatives there—the bond was preferred from afar. Taking on responsibility, however small or large was a choice and given the track record my relatives had had in the past, I was perhaps deluded into believing that they'd be there for me.

This became further evident on that mid-April day when I decided, just hours before my flight was to take off, to stay back. As the days lead up to my departure, I felt this growing sense of my impending death and as someone who has always valued the quality of life versus the quantity, I selfishly wanted more quality time in taking in all that I had received over the previous three weeks.

As I realized and expressed this, in sheer minutes, I had an overwhelming response as to what my blood relatives thought of my decision to stay. Firstly they were scared because they assumed that my staying back would add personal obligations on to them. Secondly my non-departure meant that I'd perhaps need them even more, physically, emotionally, mentally or even financially. Lastly they were concerned about my health and who would take on the responsibility for me.

Frankly, I was surprised by their tone and forwardness in wanting to send me back, but I understood that they knew they would be judged for their involvement or lack thereof in my future. I let it go and didn't let these realities change my decision to stay.

But what wounded me, more than any chemotherapy injection was a conversation with Saroj Mami. She very bluntly told me that I'd be an unwelcome guest at anyone's home. This is the same woman who for months had been telling me to come to India; the same woman who invited me for three days to her living space and spoke so highly of me, even preaching to followers of her temple that I was a real life *'Shravan'* for his mother. She now had no space left for me and had taken it upon herself to give me an ultimatum, about where I would stay and what my game plan would be, in India. There were no options being presented, this was merely the cold hard truth. I was part of a plan to show off her kind and giving nature rather than the selflessness she so frequently referred to in her *'pravachans'*.

As I hung up the phone in disbelief, I felt an incredible sense of loneliness and stupidity. Was this what I was staying back for? Having guarded my emotions to the point of not showing anyone my tears, I finally broke down. The Shahs seemed genuinely concerned and as I shared with them my apprehensions and conversations,

I asked them if they felt the same way. They consoled and reassured me that they were not judging and that they'd be there to encourage and support me on this journey. They also welcomed me to stay as long as I needed or wanted to, no strings attached.

As I went to bed that night, just about the same time I was to check-in for my flight back, I wondered what lay ahead. I knew it wasn't going to be a continuation of what I had experienced since landing in India. I managed to muster a smile as I dozed off, thinking of the irony, that in America I was supported and cared for by my friends and now as I planned to stay back in India for some time, it was likely going to be the same case.

CHAPTER 3

Holy Cow!

Climbing higher ain't an easy quest
Cause your ground is falling away
Once upon a time you knew just
What you wanted, who you were
Now you find there ain't a soul you trust
And your vision's all a blur
['Not Too Late For Love' by Beverley Knight]

The day I decided to stay back in India, I knew my real adventure was about to begin. Saroj Mami who had been so instrumental in getting me here left me feeling deserted. She seemed absolutely fearful of my decision to stay back and become a burden on her and the family. It was a bittersweet reminder of my isolation. Within minutes all the positive feelings I had had about not wanting to leave, turned to the unfortunate reality that the last three weeks were nothing more than smoke and mirrors.

However with the encouragement of the Shahs, I immediately got immersed into trying different alternative treatments. I had sat in on a couple of yoga classes with Guruji. He had expressed his interest in me, wanting to help me get in better health and be open to trying different things. I remembered a treatment the Shahs had been discussing with me called *kunjal kriya*—the act of drinking as much warm water in rapid time (normally about 1.5 litres) in the morning on an empty stomach with a pinch of salt and then immediately force vomiting it all out. The science behind the act was to remove all the old mucous and waste from the bottom of the stomach to cleanse the stomach, oesophagus and lungs.

Given that my tumours were now metastasizing into my lungs, I was a little scared to try this, but the Delhi air and pollution was so awful that I was having frequent breathing challenges. So thinking I had nothing to lose, I decided to give the practice an actual try.

The very next day I woke up at 5:15 am and prepared for the *kriya*, having already had my morning bladder and bowel movements, as my stomach needed to be as clear as possible. I stood outside with Guruji ready to help me. He advised that it's better to perform this *kriya* outside in nature while standing barefoot on grass. The closeness to nature would enrich the experience and help me to feel natural. Crouching down I held my stomach and began to drink one glass of water after another. I managed to easily gulp down about four full glasses. He pushed me on to the fifth glass, even though it felt like my stomach would not be able to take in any more, I managed to finish almost to the bottom of that glass. I then lightly inserted one finger down my throat to induce the vomiting. It took only seconds for the first shower of water to come back out. I continued the fingering a few more times till it felt like nothing remained. It was hard to estimate, but it was clear that the amount of water I had consumed was not equal to the amount that had come out. I wasn't sure if it was a success but Guruji was nevertheless pleased saying I had done well for day one. He had planned for me to do this continuously for seven days. I stood up with teary eyes and a sense of exhaustion and went back to my room to lie down. It was a strange feeling but after a short catnap, I woke up feeling refreshed.

It wasn't an instantaneous relief but there was something beyond just cleansing about the act.

Like clockwork, I continued the practice for an entire week with a sizable improvement in the amount of water I was able to take in and similarly the amount and the speed with which the water came back out. What was interesting was that while the first few days required an effort by day seven I didn't have to insert my finger in my mouth, it was an automatic reflex.

Within a week I was hooked. I noticed that my breathing had somewhat normalized and the pollution of Delhi that had bothered me to such an incredible level had somewhat subsided. I had also stopped adding salt to the water. I asked Guruji if I should continue past day seven, he mentioned that many would continue the practice through an entire month. As it was now an easy practice for me, I decided to continue the daily *kunjal kriya* practice as long as I could.

While I saw this uptick in my health, I also noticed that my ability to meditate and do some easy yoga exercises had improved. I had picked up some meditation techniques over the years, mainly through Mom. When I first got sick, many relatives and good friends had suggested various religious or spiritual practices to coincide with my treatment. Mom had adapted some of these rituals into her daily life and at times they intercepted with my routine. At points in my journey, I've questioned the presence of God, but I've never stopped believing. I credit my parents for instilling in me the faith to believe.

It doesn't matter what illness you carry with you but when you see someone else selflessly pray, meditate or focus their full attention on you, you have no choice but to believe. Whether I wanted to or not, Mom's *'dhyan'* rubbed off on me. I had seen the peace that her spirituality brought to her, and as her words and ability to communicate reduced with the progression of her brain tumour, it was truly inspiring to see that her faith was never shaken.

Perhaps the most telling sign of this was how Mom died. She passed away in the middle of the night, listening to the Jain *Navkar Mantra*, with her fingers in the *mudra* position (as though seated for meditation or prayer). So much of what led to her death, was frankly unfathomable to me, except her ability to let go and that too in such peace with her beliefs intact. I knew from that moment forward that looking inside and finding some form of peace by the day's end was a necessity for my moving forward—no matter how much time remained.

I grew up in a Jain household but never adhered much to our religious background. My father being the scientist that he was, had a very sceptical opinion of organized religion. He believed in God for sure but he also believed it was a personal choice and that community gatherings were more for show and less for the true appreciation and understanding of the religion. For him, charity began at home so he balked at witnessing relatives financing temples and shrines so as to prove their devotion.

Mom on the other hand, had come from a somewhat pure Jain household. While she was always the rebellious exception in her family, upon marriage, she basically conformed to my father's beliefs. She kept track of the holidays but other than on holy occasions not eating onions or garlic, she left the devotions to her elder siblings.

Of course life has a way of catching up with people and Mom, whether she wanted it or not, got pushed into religion after Dad's death. Seeking answers, some form of solace and also spending more time with other family members who adhered to strict Jain beliefs, she began to make certain changes in her life.

While the practicality of these changes was minimal, it was a difference I clearly noticed while living with her. As it happened, I too was trying to make sense of our new reality and it seems like I went on a theology binge purchasing every book about every religion. My curiosity increased as well and I found religion a practical topic for the two of us to converse about, while living together.

As it turned out those conversations became some of the most important, most long-lasting and impactful chats we had together. Here she shared her insecurities, her wants and the true outlook of her life so far and what she wished for her legacy. We never realized, that so quickly after Dad's death, we'd have to practically apply these discussions when I was diagnosed with cancer—I'd like to believe that we were being prepared for the next chapter of our lives.

It was on my second meeting with my oncologist that we had the conversation about the side effects of my chemotherapy and radiation. I can't say that starting a family was top priority on my agenda at that point in time, but to be told that there was a strong possibility that I would become impotent and not have biological children of my own, was something I couldn't quite wrap my head around. Thankfully I had a very wise mother who I wasn't afraid to share this news with and we decided to store my sperm for the 'just in case'.

Having lost her husband, potentially seeing her son pass away before her and to be without a family or grandchildren from him, it was a difficult reality for any mother to accept and let alone make peace with. Yet Mom continued to live her life with a smile and shortly into my treatment cycle we made a pact to always end the day with a laugh, a smile and an 'I love you'. It was how I said my final goodbye to her years later and I continue to do this even without her physical presence here.

These beliefs that Mom valued, strongly resonated in me. Perhaps it was that faith which ultimately allowed me to fly; to leave the New York area and come to India. Perhaps it was the deciding factor of wanting to extend my trip. Perhaps it was also the driving force of my new found fascination and willingness to wake up each morning and begin my day with the *kunjal kriya* and then meditate.

I started off with what I knew. I knew the *Navkar Mantra* and recited that with eyes closed 108 times in the morning and then again before going to sleep. It was meant to be a way of self-purification. The *mantra* itself speaks of success, abundance, control and happiness. It was a challenge the first few nights. My mind would wander, and I would focus on the counting but then I'd lose track. Though slowly and surely, I found a groove and like clockwork the repetition of the *mantra* became a routine, without thought or interruptions. I was pleasantly surprised that as I got into a pattern, I began to let go of the many images that didn't just haunt me at night but rather stayed with me while awake too.

As distraught as I was when my father died unexpectedly, despite our full confidence in his routine surgery procedure, I had lost any sense of fear with the passing of my mother. Yet the images, those final moments lingered with me. Not so much for what it took me back to, but rather, what I saw ahead for myself.

Having lost the main decision makers in my life, it was up to me to plan the end for myself. I had seen enough to know what I wanted and what I did not. As my own medical advocate, I had already drafted every scenario and what action should be taken. My course of action in the US was already set, but being in India, I was facing a challenge. Whereas I had security while staying with the Shah's, I had to face the reality that if my health deteriorated and needed constant medical attention—what then? And if my health spiralled down quickly—what then?

I had confided in a dear friend of mine, Noor from high school, who was waiting for her visa to shift to London and join her husband (thankfully she was in New Delhi during this time frame). Together we began researching palliative care options in India. We were surprised to see the lack of facilities available. Most doctors and hospitals treated the disease and then individuals either fought till the end at the hospital itself or were taken to their respective homes for their final moments.

Those without family were generally taken in by relatives or someone within the community willing to offer this last stage of kindness, for the sickly individual. Still, there are some who did not even have that luxury. We found a limited number of spaces for the dying elderly, as opposed to a traditional 'nursing home' type facility, something rather commonplace in America.

As I continued my research, I thought about the hospital Pooja Massi had told me about. I wondered if that hospital in Gujarat offered such facilities. I managed to google 'cow hospital Gujarat' as that's all I remembered. What showed up was a website with photos identical to the ones in the magazine and again everything was written in Gujarati. Looking at the facility online, I was relieved to see that the campus was quite lovely and my eyes were immediately drawn to the cows. They looked different than the ones I had seen on the roads of Delhi and Mumbai.

I thought about asking someone to translate the writing and perhaps get me more information about the hospital. As it turns out, my cousin Deena (Sapna Massi's daughter) had been checking up on me and I asked her about the place. Within a few hours, by some order of a miracle it seems, she got back to me and told me that the trustees of the hospital were friends of the family. They got me a number to call and I was truly in disbelief as to how easy it had been to find out about the place.

I next inquired with another cousin of mine, Indu who lived near the hospital in Surat Gujarat, to see if she knew anything about the place. She seemed quite judgmental saying it was meant for poor villagers and after undergoing treatment in America, why would I even want to consider this hospital?

It was a valid point. Somewhere in the process of my daily *kunjal kriya* and meditation, I began to feel better. The improvement in my health encouraged me to further explore alternative options for treatment. I had already been told that the Ayurvedic pills I had been taking in the US were commensurate with what any Ayurvedic doctor would prescribe to me in India. I had thought about traveling to see a doctor in Kerala who worked with cancer patients but honestly, my focus was more on looking for treatments for my palliative care, as opposed to doctors, camps and treatments that promised to cure the disease.

As Noor and I put our hats together and thought about my long-term plans for staying in India—the cow hospital seemed like a worthwhile exploration. I began to publicly mention my interest in the eleven-day course I was told about, by the trustee over the phone. I didn't want to rush it though as I was about two weeks into my daily morning routine and had it in mind that I wanted to accomplish a full month of the practice before moving onto the next treatment.

It's strange that things we hear in a passing conversation can become something real and ultimately change our path. As I started to begin a routine, I had no idea that what I was actually setting up was a way of life for myself. I was incredibly blessed that the Shah's home had certain comforts, things that most places would not have permitted or perhaps enriched me with—from twenty four hour maid attention to a vast outdoor space with a jogger's path and swimming pool to a kitchen staff that made me basically any food I wanted to eat.

The majority of the vegetables were grown just outside my guest room in the garden. Literally, just prior to cooking, the vegetables would be taken out and prepared for us, and that too all organic. From *karela* to *lauki* to *kaddu*—I was eating better than ever—a simple enhanced diet without chemicals or pesticides.

As an avid foodie I was able to share recipes in the kitchen and prepare dishes that reminded me of home. As I flipped through my rolodex of dishes, I realized that the years of treatment and awareness that I had developed in terms of food and nutrition, had made me somewhat of a 'Rain Man' expert, when it came to nutritional value and nutritional balance. I hadn't necessarily stuck to a specific diet over the years, but I had picked up titbits along the way about the importance of a balanced diet and treating food as medicine.

The challenge and with that the blessing of coming to India, was the introduction to so many additional fruits, vegetables and types of grains that I was not accustomed to incorporating into my meals in America. Of course, there was the added change that I was not cooking for myself.

I could suggest or request but I was not ultimately the one preparing my meals. I took each meal that I didn't make myself as an opportunity to learn something additional about the food I was eating, whether it was finding out the ingredients, suggesting, adding or omitting ingredients from that recipe or finding substitutes to make the dish different (and ideally healthier).

I enjoyed cooking, but the philosophy of food as medicine, really got incorporated into my way of life after my first round of cancer and while my mother was undergoing chemotherapy. As a result of her brain tumour she was on a high dose of steroids. Being pre-diabetic the steroids immediately affected her blood sugar, I had to administer her insulin and check her sugar levels prior to each meal. Additionally, she was participating in a clinical trial for an autonomous stem-cell transplant. In essence, her stem cells would be extracted, she'd undergo a high intensity chemotherapy regimen in the hospital that would ideally rid her body of cancer and then she'd have her stem cells transplanted back, with the goal that the cancer would no longer be present in her system.

It was a bold option but all the signs post her diagnoses were so positive that the oncology team was 'hopefully optimistic'. Traditionally with malignant tumours the idea of remission or living with an indefinite time frame is unheard of, but it was presented to us so we jumped at the opportunity. Aware of the reality, Mom and I knew that very few patients even have reports that permit something like this—we had to give it a try.

Of course as the treatments went on and the transplant lingered in the future, we prepared for the next steps. We met other patients and caregivers who had gone through the process and got to learn first-hand the complexities of this new lease on life, granted to a select few in the world.

One of the most interesting aspects of the process was that this new life would result in zero immunity at start. As a result the chances of acquiring an infection were million-fold higher. Restrictions of every kind were in place to prevent this from happening. From wearing a mask at most times to being hospitalized the first month, while living literally in a bubble till blood counts and immunity had reached a somewhat decent level to interact with others, to strict food restrictions to avoid any kind of infection—it was somewhat shocking the lengths to which someone would be required to go to get their life back.

Mom and I most feared the food aspect of the treatment. No fresh fruits or vegetables were permitted. There was a restriction on dairy intake. Basically all food must be processed to the point that there was no chance of bacteria. For a lifelong vegetarian, the idea of giving up fresh fruits and vegetables, the staple of our diet was a challenge we hadn't really thought out as we signed up for the treatment. We had also seen how our cancer diet, that incorporated fresh organic produce; restrictions on white sugar, white flour and white salt had resulted in stellar track records for both of us with limited side effects, no constipation, no diarrhoea, no indigestion and no nausea.

Sadly, the progression of my mother's cancer, took away her chances from continuing with the trial and being able to do the stem-cell transplant. But there was a plus side, my mother's diet maintained. We watched so many of our patient friends struggle, it's a wonder how someone given a new lease on life has to start over with frozen dishes, canned fruit and processed cheeses, meats and breads. Yet the miracle of life is that this diet is what is required when undergoing such a treatment.

Being a vegetarian in India and being exposed to such a large variety of additional options, offered me ample opportunity to add further to the food with my medicinal approach. Of course I was fortunate to live in a bubble at the Shah's farmhouse. I was living a life of luxury there, not confined by the restrictions of the local market and the understanding of individuals who are not open to trying new items.

While I had adjusted to living there, I knew my time there couldn't be permanent as their own travels began. Since they had to close down the house given its grand size, I was to shift for a few days to Mom's eldest sister Jyoti Massi's place in Old Delhi (she had three sons and I was to stay with my cousins). I had spoken to them and they were open to my coming but something inside me didn't feel right. Halfway through my *kunjal kriya* course, I knew I needed to keep at it and I couldn't head to Mumbai (to make my way to the cow hospital) until I had finished this course. I could have done it anywhere but the idea of finishing what I had started in one place felt like the right thing to do.

Additionally, I was still in the investigative stage. I felt the need to let my relatives in on a bit and let them know what I was thinking for both the immediate and long-term future. I didn't necessarily need them but I needed to see what help was there, if any, and whether I would at least have a support system in place if I chose Delhi to be the place I opted to stay and try these options out.

As I sat in the cab heading out, I thought about the countless car rides I had made over the years. I had yet again lost a home. As much as I knew it was not in the hands of the Shahs—the longing to have a place that was permanent—living outside the suitcase seemed like an impossible task in India for me. I was determined to try out varied treatments, to learn and go back. Of course, there was still a long way between the cows and me.

CHAPTER 4

Dead Man Walking

The taste of love
The more you get the more you want.
And all because
The only reason is just because
It all makes sense
When you're near it all makes sense
['Sense' by Lightning Seeds]

Sometimes an environment can be toxic. The week I spent with my cousins proved that. The home where I had spent countless summers, the family who were so close to me that there never needed to be an invitation ever—I felt like a stranger visiting their home.

Sure, a lot of things had built up to this awkwardness in the relationship. First, the link was primarily based on my parents and specifically with Mom. Second, as the youngest cousin on her side, I was always seen as the baby, incapable of making adult decisions and not having the ability to take care of others or even myself. Third, they had helped us financially. Amidst the years of cancer treatments, I accepted this offered generosity with the goal of repayment upon my improved health. As that day continually went past any anticipated recovery date, my reality got bleaker. Getting closer to death, dying was the faster sure shot way to clearing these debts.

Adding further fuel to the fire was that my travels to India decreased significantly after the death of my father. While the years away were justified by illnesses, there was little interaction and a majority of that communication was through Mom until she fell ill and as her sole caregiver, I did not have the capacity to stay in touch with anyone during her treatment.

I tried my best to involve them by sending thorough emails about our journey and letting them in on details I knew were beyond their comprehension. Informing every one of the same information through one channel permitted me to focus on one thing, Mom's health and positive mental condition. I had seen how miscommunication and lack of knowledge created so much hearsay and false truth, that to be able to correct everyone would have been a fulltime job.

Arriving at Jyoti Massi's home without any warm welcome (in stark contrast to my arrival there just weeks prior on my initial visit) was my first red flag. Additionally, there was major renovation going on at their place, so I was a little alarmed about the space. However they were very accommodating in giving me a room and tending to my needs. There were no formalities per se but it felt formal. I couldn't pinpoint what exactly made it feel different but it just did.

We did get to share stories about the time that had passed since we last met. It's hard to fill in people though on an experience you yourself remain unsure about. I had a challenge discussing certain truths, because I was still in denial. I was living with false hope and despite every inch of my body wanting to do the right thing, I was also in a survival mode that was engraved in me and I feared letting go would close doors rather than open them. I felt closer to death than life and I had held onto the threat of an impending death, as a way to justify my behaviour and corresponding actions.

Perhaps, my pig-headedness in being unwilling to share this reality was the cause of the cold treatment. Perhaps, this was my method of rationalising the new way in which I was being treated. Perhaps, it may have been just as easy if everyone had been busy in their own respective lives and I was a welcome guest. Without a confirmed return date, I was a time bomb with no permanent space set, inviting me in would prove indefinite.

All evidence pointed towards the latter being the case. Jyoti Massi flatly told me that I had made the wrong decision to stay in India and that nobody would care for me here, so I should just quietly go back and accept whatever life has in store for me, in my own home. It was a brutal truth but I knew it was coming from a place of wisdom. This is a woman who managed eighty plus years and knew the reality of family responsibility and the truths behind the facades of invitations and offers to help.

Still I tried to ensure my time there was well spent. I investigated further into the cow hospital. I found out that there was no hospice or palliative care available there but it was a growing facility. I actually found some research that debated the effectiveness of cow urine (I saw there was some study being done in Europe and at a prominent hospital in Dallas, Texas) that made me even more curious and determined.

Sharing this information with my cousins, I saw that there was somewhat of a willingness to offer me long-term support if I chose to stay in Delhi. Provided, of course, I knew what I was going to do. I didn't like the restrictions of the help. I was used to making decisions in the moment, of being my own advocate. Knowing full well that my health could change at the drop of a hat, I needed to think about my time in a different light. Maybe I could travel the country and try different treatments, then find one place and make it a more permanent setting for me.

However I had stopped making any real plans, as living in the moment over the last few years had been the only way to retain my sanity. Whether concern or curiosity or a combination of the two drove the conversation—coming to India and not having a real foundation was a challenge.

All this became secondary fodder, as the time at my cousin's place became physically challenging for me. Perhaps as a result of the construction work going underway, the overall dust and cleanliness of the home, my ongoing *kunjal kriya*, my potentially developing tumours or even the withdrawal symptoms after having stopped my maintenance drugs by deciding to stay back in India, I was having breathing difficulties like I had never experienced before.

I first fought the uncontrollable cough fits with medicines, then simply took rest and avoided going out, but the breathing was becoming that much more of an effort. Finally one evening I started to cough and felt uneasy alongside it. All the 'don't worry I'm fine 'and 'nothing will happen this suddenly' faded away in an instant. I saw the state of panic that covered the faces of my cousins. They were concerned for my health but they were also aware of the reality that my illness would fall unfairly under their guise, because they were there at the start.

That's the pitfall of large families. In good times everyone wants to be there. In bad times it's a ghost town. The core problem is if anyone does step up, the others collectively opt out, given that that person had already offered a hand. It's ironic that in a large family rather than feeling safety in numbers, there's a tendency to feel isolated as most are concerned as to why others in the family are not stepping up as opposed to themselves.

As I stood in my cousin's hall gasping for breath, they prepared to rush me to the hospital. I became so light headed that for a moment I thought I was having a heart attack and that I would die right there. I stood there unsure of what to do next. Kishore *Massa* had been a stroke victim several years back and his age and diminishing health had resulted in the almost daily use of a nebuliser. My cousin smartly thought to get the machine and have me breathe through it. I had eased up slightly quite unsure of what had transpired but I placed the nebulizer over my mouth and nose and slowly calmed myself down as I recited the *Navkar Mantra* repeatedly.

At that moment, in that instance, I knew that I wasn't going to be a burden on any of my loved ones. All the feelings of pain, hurt and sadness that coated my heart went away. I realized that my end needed to be my end and that I shouldn't take advantage of someone else's kindness. If I was going to stay in India, I was going to have to do it for myself and not take anything or anyone for granted. I had taken care of myself in America—I'd have to do the same here.

I spent the next couple of days more determined than ever, to make my way to Mumbai and onwards to the cow hospital. I had noticed an improvement with the nebulizer and upon returning to the Shah's place a week later, a far less polluted environment in all ways, there was clearly marked progress.

My breathing was much lighter and the *kunjal kriya* had become an automatic response. I had coordinated with my cousin Deena about the hospital, and I planned to etch out the details upon reaching Mumbai, anxious to start this leg of my journey. I had also simultaneously found out about two organizations in Mumbai that housed terminal patients, just in case.

While I had agreed to stay at Meena *Chachi's* place, I was doing my best to ensure a short stay. She had room to spare as her son (and his immediate family) was vacationing in the United States. At this point I was aware of my plague-like presence at people's homes, so I wanted to try and do what I could on my own or without the need of involvement from relatives. Still the trip that lay ahead required their assistance.

As I packed for my trip, I had a conversation with the Shahs who seemed optimistic about my next steps. They were confident that they'd see me in a few weeks after my time with the cows. I too anticipated a quick return. With hopes of learning as much as possible, healing however best I could and then making the return trip back to America in improved health, thanks to all the healing alternative paths and powers of India.

Perhaps my fate had something additional left for me to see before moving forward. As I was packing to head to Mumbai, I got a call that Mom's eldest brother Manish Mama, had passed away. It wasn't unexpected as he had been sick on and off, but he was never critical. I had planned to go visit him in the hospital only to learn that he died that morning itself. I made my way to his home where his body had been taken for pre-cremation ceremonies. There was a certain irony in the fact that Manish Mama was the only relative within my reach that I had not gotten to meet since coming to India. We spoke on the phone and I knew he was eager to meet me. My cousins informed me that he had grieved significantly when Mom passed away. It was a bittersweet experience to be there for his last rites.

I had never actually participated in a cremation ceremony in India. It was unlike anything I had experienced. Both my parent's deaths and the subsequent days were so drastically different from one another, yet both so diametrically opposite from an Indian death, it was indeed overwhelming.

With each hug that was had, every tear that was shed, I wondered about Mom's death. Did her death create such a similar rippling effect? Mom's death was so isolated, as I was the only one there. Dad's brother, his wife and their son were the only people there at the cremation. I chose it to be that way. Unlike my father's unexpected death, Mom's death was a long time coming. Everyone was aware of her prognosis and I had given ample time and information to all the people in her life about this impending moment.

I honestly did not feel the need to have anyone there who had not chosen to be there for her. We had conversations about our death and what we would want to happen immediately afterwards. She was someone who didn't look back with regrets. She was a grateful woman who proved in her dying moments that she was at peace. I knew she deserved a celebration of her life, a time that her near and dear ones could come together and honour her in the way that she deserved. There would be tears but they'd be mirrored by laughter.

I thought about myself, standing in the funeral homes of both my parents and then seeing the circus of people surrounding Manish Mama, as they prepared to take him for the cremation. I wasn't sure what I preferred, I'm not sure there is a need to choose what is better, but there is one thing—the pink elephant in my mind was that I was witnessing potentially what would become of me if my time came to an end, in India.

It got further cemented upon reaching the crematory. I was surprised that the space was unlike what I had seen in films. While the bodies were still dressed and prepared traditionally, it was now an electric burner, similar to the ones I had said farewell to both my parent's bodies in America. The only difference of course, was that I wasn't pressing the button and there certainly were a lot more people here.

But as I stood in silence witnessing this, I heard mobile phones ring. I saw men having conversations about random things unrelated to Manish Mama's death. It took me right back to Dad's cremation. I remember looking out to the many men that stood around me. I hardly knew them. Dad had died far far away from any of the places he called home. He was lucky to have them there and I should feel thankful to have had the strength of numbers, but that moment is forever etched in my head—that ironic moment of being there with a swarm of strangers saying goodbye, when I knew how so many who knew him around the world, were grieving for him.

Manish Mama's death felt like a gift to me. Perhaps he and I were not meant to meet but there was a reason I stayed back, I had to be there to say goodbye to him. I had already settled in my head that I was going to return to America after visiting the cow hospital and any other treatment that perhaps fell my way in the coming time frame. Ultimately—I wanted to close my eyes back home. Both my parents had had me there for them. While they were always with me in spirit, I knew I wanted to be near them physically at death. As silly as it sounds knowing that my ashes would also be spread in that same water in New York—perhaps we'd all be together again.

As I left the crematory, I heard the whispers of distant relatives. They were discussing my cancer. I wondered if their minds were as toxic as mine got once in a while, wondering if I was next. While I was going to try my best to not let that happen—death is something out of anyone's control.

I spent that night crying uncontrollably. I wasn't sure exactly what I was crying for, but just as my *kunjal* was letting out all the waste that had accumulated over years of chemotherapies and steroids and so many other things, so too were these tears. I was letting out so many emotions, perhaps it was preparing me for my next destination.

I woke up the next day feeling like some weight had been lifted off my shoulders. As I headed to the airport to catch my flight to Mumbai for the second time on this trip to India, I felt this sense of movement, almost like the tides were turning. I needed to make each moment in India count—I was living in a state of why not and my excitement about trying something new was numbing the pain of waiting.

CHAPTER 5

The Waiting Game

Don't believe the things
You tell yourself late at night
You are your worst enemy
You will lose the fight
['Parachute' by Cheryl Cole]

When I landed in Mumbai I had one singular mission, to get myself to the cow hospital in Sevak, Gujarat. I had spoken to my Meena Chachi who insisted I stay a few days with her. I was hoping I'd be able to make my official arrangements for the hospital in a day or so. In reality, the three and a half hour trip took me eleven days.

My cousin Deena, who knew one of the trustees, was traveling overseas so it became a challenge for me to coordinate my trip. I began making calls to all the family members in Mumbai who had gone out of their way just a few weeks prior to come and see me and I told them of my plans. Everyone seemed beyond sceptical and also seemed rather uninterested in my plans.

As the hospital was in Gujarat and the website was written in Gujarati, I knew I needed someone to at least accompany me there through check-in and then I'd be able to manage things. But every conversation left ample room for silence that spoke volumes as far as the road ahead was concerned.

Thankfully, as luck would have it, Noor was visiting Mumbai and as I tried to figure out the best way to move forward, we met to decipher all that had been transpiring with my family. It's a strange thing, we had been in touch on and off over the years but our friendship was rooted in a common past. We hadn't really been integral in each other's lives since high school but the faith and confidence she had in me, made all the negative energy around me feel like just white noise. It is true—sometimes all you need is just one friend.

In one afternoon, I was rejuvenated and ready to find a way no matter what, to make my way to Sevak. Even though I had promised myself not to ask for help, I decided to change my strategy with my relatives. Rather than beating around the bush and informing them of what my plans were, I left no room for interpretation and directly asked them to accompany me to the hospital and then they could head back the same day if they wished. Of course if they wanted to stay, I wouldn't have said no either.

But every call ended with the same response. It wasn't a 'no' but each call concluded with an open-ended 'we'll think about it and get back to you'. As I waited for replies, hours turned to days. It became evident that despite my direct plea and effort, I wasn't going to have anyone from my family accompany me to the cow hospital.

I voiced my frustration to Sapna Massi, as she was the only elderly relative who had actually spun the news positively, that I was planning to extend my stay in India. She probably didn't even realize how significant a gesture that was for me. She had her own set of complications. In her mid-seventies she was the waning Queen Bee of her family. With Manav Massa's own challenging health issues and a fulltime aide assisting him on his day-to-day tasks, Sapna Massi had her hands full handling her own and her husband's health. Like most of my relatives she lived with her son Kushal, his wife and their two small children. Unfortunately like most family driven television dramatizations—the same conflicts existed.

Sapna Massi being the perceptive woman she has always been, was mindful of her evolving position within her family. She managed to care for Manav Massa and her own needs and whatever else she could do to keep busy and manage the household without drama. But each generation has different needs and wants. The usual nighttime soaps she'd watch every night on the television seemed to be re-enacted within their flat. The standard arguments about how to raise the grandchildren, when and what to eat, going out and passing along responsibilities—I was privy to a real life *'saas-bahu'* serial just visiting them.

Yet despite her far too complicated life, she always made time for my phone calls. She seemed utterly peeved and frankly quite shocked at the ambivalence the family was showing for simply dropping me off to Sevak. She had her own reasoning for why the family was behaving in such a manner. To put it bluntly, which she always was, she told me that no one had the time or interest in helping me. She went on to further say that my 'story' wasn't adding up and that there were questions.

I couldn't do anything but laugh. In the many years that I had been a patient, I had been questioned about many things—work, insurance, money, marriage, love—but I had never been questioned about my health.

It was valid to have questions, but then to have questions and then to not actually have a conversation with the individual concerned, is what I couldn't understand.

As Sapna Massi explained, my unwillingness to share my medical records with select members of the family (who in turn would share everything with one another) was the sticking point. In reality I had actually shared a limited set of records with her daughter, Richa, the sole doctor in our family.

Richa was genuinely concerned with my medical case when I arrived in India. It was a blessing that I actually got to see her and discuss my history with her on my initial visit to Mumbai. She had offered, no questions asked, the opportunity for me to come and stay with her in Bangalore and that she and her husband would care for me for as long as I had. It was an incredible offer and quite tempting.

As I seriously considered joining her in Bangalore, where she managed a hospital, I thought about what had brought me to India. While sharing some of my recent medical history with her, I actually realized what I wanted. I expressed to her that I was tired and that I did not want to step back into the allopathic world. After years at the best hospitals, top doctors and countless medications and treatments, I didn't want to meet yet another doctor and do more tests to ultimately receive the same news.

My doctor's letter from America still lingered in my head. I had not shared its contents with anyone till that point. As I forwarded it to her, I wanted to understand that as much as I appreciated her willingness to help—I was on another journey.

My continued time in India needed to matter. I had to do things that I had not done before. It could not be the main road travelled anymore, I needed to find another route, a scenic one if I could find it, exploring options where I didn't know the results. And frankly, after the time spent with relatives in their homes, I was weary of staying long term anywhere, however genuine the offer.

I was truly thankful to Richa though, as she did give me confidence about one specific fear that I still had, that if things went quickly downhill health wise, I'd have someone willing to be there for me who I know would not unequivocally carry the same judgment.

Sapna Massi endorsed Richa's offer. As she explained why, the image that I had versus what was then relayed to me broke my confidence. Richa had received calls from other relatives and found it completely acceptable to discuss my medical history with them, despite my lack of consent. This hit me hard as I was not used to hearing my case being shared like an open newsletter.

To be honest, I wouldn't have minded sharing all of my medical history with any one of my relatives if I saw even a shred of willingness to listen, to provide genuine empathy or anything more than just an unsolicited opinion.

I never lost a night of sleep after Mom's death. Her peaceful state of mind at the time of her death was the ideal picture of a sleeping beauty. While I never doubted the decisions we had made upon her cancer diagnosis, I realized as all this transpired, that it was godsend that I hadn't brought my mother to India for her final chapter.

It's something to realize that your last days are better spent away from your family and loved ones. Concern and care are two separate matters. No matter how well intentioned people may be—they have short attention spans and diseases like cancer are long-term battles The sad truth about this reality was that when I voiced these thoughts to Sapna Massi and then to Meena chachi, they both agreed.

They both had such fond memories of my visits as a child, I could see the heartbreak and disappointment in their eyes. They wanted to help, they wanted to be there, but they were bound by their duties to their immediate family. And ultimately just as I was on a journey of self-preservation, so too were they.

I felt defeated. With each passing day I was getting more and more negative, thinking even when I want to share my medical case and I'm asking for help, why is no one there for me? Sapna Massi took my sadness to heart and after countless days of hearing me literally beg someone to accompany me to the hospital, she offered to take me.

I was hesitant to accept her offer, in her condition, but she was adamant. She too felt it was unacceptable that no one on either side of my family was willing to take me to a hospital, to get better. She stepped up and it seemed like finally the wait was going to be over.

It's a funny thing, I'm not sure if the struggle to get to the point of leaving for Sevak may have single-handedly increased my faith in what the hospital had to offer. Going there as a sceptic, I was willing to try anything, I mean anything—to alleviate or maybe slow down my cancer progression. Call after call, day after day, the more I spoke aloud about the facility, the more I began to actually believe that what awaited me there was worth believing in.

I had continued my *kunjal kriya* all those days in Mumbai and as I saw myself on a steady climb of improvement, I was determined to find additional treatments and options for my daily routine. It may have been a small change but it was a noticeable one. As I packed my bag—figuring out what to take with me for my eleven day stay—Sapna Massi seemed to be optimistic about my future as well.

In that moment I felt Mom inside of her, channelling that pure positive energy and the selflessness I had reserved only for my parents. I wasn't exactly sure if I'd get better or I'd visit the hospital and return right back with her immediately, thinking this wasn't for me, but I too felt hope alongside my curiosity.

As it turned out, by the time of my journey to the hospital, Deena had returned from her trip abroad and decided to come along with her mother and her other sister Naina—making it a true family affair. I knew their interest was more in making sure their mother would be okay, but that was fine with me. After all, I had been in the same position just a short while before with Mom. Finally the waiting game was over.

CHAPTER 6

No Attendant Necessary

God I can't do this anymore
Thought I'll be laid down on the floor
As many feet walk through the door
I'm not alone

['I'm Not Alone' by Calvin Harris]

There was excitement about my trip to the hospital, dare say it almost felt like I was being taken to summer camp. Sapna Massi and my two cousins had come over the night before and we spent half the night reminiscing about our childhood days. It was the perfect setup for our impending early morning trip.

I did my kunjal one last time and we were on our way. The three and a half hour trip was a non-stop chat fest and for the first time since deciding to stay back in India I felt that familial connection again. In that moment, I felt lucky to have loved ones who were there for me, willing to take the time out of their schedules to do something for me and support my medical decisions, rather than question them or make me question myself.

The drive itself was rather smooth as we beat the Mumbai rush hour traffic. I was impressed at the highway and was surprised at the amount of elaborate eateries along the highway, replicating the multi-cuisine restaurants of the city. Soon, within a few kilometres my cousin noticed a sign in Gujarati 'Laxmiprasad Cancer

Hospital'. We had finally arrived at the next stop in my journey.

For the first time in my life I was both curious and incredibly scared. I had literally begged my way to getting here and as I got out of the car and looked at a beautiful campus with signs pointing in different directions, none of which I could read—I wondered what the hell I was thinking.

Upon entering the campus it was evident that this was no normal hospital. Despite the lavish greenery and lush landscaping, I noticed the rows of shoes and sandals outside the registration office. As Deena went inside to inquire about my status, Sapna Massi and Naina waited outside and started to figure out what building was what.

The hospital was a Jain institution. Just opposite the reception I could see three female *sadhus* sitting in the *apasra*, near the *mandir*. I knew enough to tell they were my faction of Jains, *Sthanakvasi*. Growing up I hadn't paid much attention, other than the fact that I knew my family of Jains did not believe in *murti puja*, praying to any statue. We'd instead go and get blessings from *maharajis*, dressed in white and their mouths covered with a white cloth.

As Sapna Massi went to get their blessings, Deena returned telling me that I was registered and now I'd have to go to the hospital entrance where the doctors would meet me, look over my medical records and grant me admission. The cost was one rupee and there was a refundable deposit of thousand rupees for the eleven day stay.

As we walked the campus to the front entrance of the hospital, I noticed my first set of cancer patients, since arriving in India. At first glance three things became apparent, most of the patients were suffering from progressed stages of the disease; they were clearly from rural areas of India and finally they did not come from wealthy households.

As we went to check-in, I was to fill out a full medical history sheet and then a medical consent form, of course, it was all written in Gujarati. Thankfully Deena served as translator and filled out all the forms appropriately.

I felt somewhat frozen in the moment. As much as I was aware that the hospital promised an eleven day cure to cancer, I wondered if I had signed up for a scam of some sort. As we waited for our turn with the doctors, our process was interrupted. The administrator informed us that I could not stay at the hospital without an attendant. A caregiver was required for the entire duration of the stay, to ensure that I was medically okay and to manage and support my treatment while there.

In all the conversations leading up to my arrival at the hospital, this was something I was frankly not aware of. It made sense that there'd be such a rule but I simply thought someone was required to check me in and be there again at my discharge time. My cousins, Sapna Massi and I discussed this. Clearly the three of them could not stay there with me on such short notice. Regardless, they were the matriarchs of their own respective households. Sapna Massi at her age would not be able to stay with me, while both my cousins had elderly in-laws, husbands and children to care for at home. The fact of the matter was that I knew in reality that taking out even one day from their schedule to do this for me was quite the grand act.

I insisted with the administrator, citing my being alone and not having anyone who would be able to stay with me. Thankfully our discussion paused as the doctors were ready to see me. Deena and I went inside. It was a

53

4 × 4 room and besides an eye chart nothing about the room resembled any doctor's office I'd ever seen. Whereas I was used to seeing plastic human skeletons and organ diagrams and medical degree certificates on the wall, here I saw rather large posters of the various species of holy cows. It was fascinating to see this, but again, besides the picture I couldn't understand anything as the text was in Gujarati.

The doctor asked to see my medical records, which I went ahead and showed him. He thoroughly read through the letters, blood reports and such, then started asking me questions off a rather simple table. As I answered a yes or no, I realized what was being asked were symptoms and side effects. He began to check off certain medications and write in other names on the bottom of a sheet that seemed to be a pre-set medicine list. I was surprised that he didn't ask me much about my history and within ten minutes or so had written up my treatment course for the eleven days. He went on to explain the nurse's station where I'd get my medicines and other items as needed for different treatments. I pleaded with him if I could have the medications that I'd be taking written in English, so I understood exactly what they were. He suggested that I meet with the medications specialist who could translate whatever I needed much more quickly.

As I was trying to figure out what exactly I had signed up for and if I was ready to fight this challenge alone, one of the trustees, Umeshbhai paid a visit to the office. He had actually been called to meet with me, as his brother was my cousin's contact and he wanted to make sure everything was okay with my admission process. However by the time he introduced himself to us he had already found out that I did not have an attendant, so the conversation directly addressed that. He grabbed my newly created file and began to read my chart.

Deena introduced herself and tried to explain our dilemma. He seemed rather amused as she went on with what he deemed as excuses and then vehemently opposed my staying at the hospital without an attendant. His rationale was valid, he argued that someone taking new medications, undertaking treatment—if something was to happen—who will be there. As this was not a traditional hospital and strictly Ayurvedic, the hospital needed an assurance that every patient had an advocate supporting the patient, caring for them at all times in case of complications, stresses or especially emergencies.

As we realized that we couldn't really argue against the policy, my cousin Deena suggested if other cousins could made trips and take turns to be with me. He seemed hesitant and suggested we strategize and get back to him. Deena then tried to play the relation card and requested if an exception could be made. While adamantly opposed to any justification, it became apparent to me that he had not heard this for the first time. With that, my cousin called her contact to see if he could override this decision.

As she spoke to him I updated Sapna Massi and Naina on what had transpired. They seemed rather disappointed, but in a small way relieved that the hospital was at least behaving in a mature legitimate manner. Sapna Massi suggested I call my cousin who lived in Surat approximately 70 kms away from the hospital. She thought given the close proximity she'd be the best bet for at least coming by to check up on me. I was a bit hesitant, as I already knew that even when I wanted information about the hospital, she was unwilling to find out anything in regards to the place.

As my cousin finished the call with her contact, it seemed her influence and relationship trumped the warnings of Umeshbhai. With the call it was apparent that I would be able to stay. That didn't stop the trustee from verbally berating my family. It was for the first time I heard someone so strongly advocate the lunacy that had surrounded me for so much of my trip and time with my relatives. He expressed his belief that this was the time for everyone to come together and be there for me—for them not to think about anything else—but to focus on getting me healthy and staying positive.

He then went one step further, he grabbed my medical file and started to read the letter from my doctor—that letter which haunted me—the one that put the rest of my life on an active timer. He asked Sapna Massi if she felt comfortable leaving someone with only 'six months' by himself? Then he looked at my cousins and proclaimed, 'the hospitals have given up hope, you have no hope... but I do. We do.'

It was the first time that I heard my letter read aloud publicly. It was also the first time those words were shared with my family. All the walls I had created around myself to protect my emotions and not to let anyone actually get to me, finally chipped away—I was left grasping for air. As I saw the trustee go on and on, my family tucked away in a sense of shame and guilt. I knew the reality though, that these were not the individuals who deserved the berating, as they were the ones who had actually escorted me here. I jumped in and suggested I forget about the hospital and wait till I had a friend from the United States come and join me. I was confident that if I reached out, I'd have many of those same friends who had been there for me back home, fly across the world to be here with me.

Hearing this the trustee saw my commitment and also my helpless situation. While having already caved in, he now seemed to be on my side and said that there was no need to go back and return at a later point. He suggested to my relatives that they go back and strategize and have someone come meet me at the hospital in a day or two. Until then they'd take responsibility for me.

With hesitation we all agreed. The trustee went to find out if he could get me a room partner who spoke English to at least make my life a little easier. With that my room was assigned and Sapna Massi and cousins escorted me to my room. It was on the second floor. As I entered my new home, I noticed a relatively young woman with her mother, who was clearly in a great deal of pain. We exchanged pleasantries and I began to settle into my room. It was a rather simple room. One cot was for the patient and one for the caregiver. There was one end table and a common sink and then two attached bathrooms. It was clean and there seemed to be a nice breeze coming in from the window. As I put my luggage in place, I knew it was time to say goodbye to my family.

I walked them out of the hospital and thought about our morning ride. We had laughed our way to the hospital but as we said goodbye, there was a genuine concern on both sides. In them I could see a level of guilt, concern and shame. For me, there was fear of the unknown, yet there was a level of optimism. Perhaps it was a renewed sense of wishful thinking as well, but I believed that Sapna Massi and cousins would actually go back and get me set up here with other family. Perhaps all the barricades I had set up for myself might have just come tumbling down. I was in my most vulnerable state. Alone in the hospital, getting treatment, without any caregiver—this was a test not just for me—but also for my family. I hugged Sapna Massi and she gave me her blessings with tears in her eyes. I saw Mom in her but I also saw a woman trapped within the confines of her restricted familial structure.

It may not have been everything that I needed but saying goodbye to her and seeing those selfless tears come down, I felt that my next chapter was at least starting or in hindsight, ending with love.

CHAPTER 7

Military Medicine

I can't stand this indecision
['Everybody Wants To Rule The World' by Tears For Fears]

Ayurveda and the army are rarely ever used in the same sentence, but at the hospital the two were synonymous. Our routines were so detailed and our time schedule so specific—sometimes it felt like we were in cancer boot camp receiving military medicine.

Hospitals run more efficiently when things are organized and run on time. This reality however, often doesn't match up because there are always unexpected delays. But the sign of a good hospital is when those unexpected delays do not derail the routine. In fact, the best hospitals have these delays factored in so they know how to handle any and all complications that may arise and handle them effectively.

To see this principle carried out so brilliantly at the Laxmiprasad Hospital was frankly beyond shocking for me. All my assumptions about the lack of time sensitivity in India flew out of the window, seeing that the hospital was run on such a strict schedule. It was truly a sight to be seen.

The minute we registered and checked into our room we were escorted to the Nurse's station and given a detailed schedule of all of the activities, our medicines and the meal timings.

As everything at the hospital was written in Gujarati, I had to wait for one of the quasi-English speaking nurses

59

(sisters as they were called there) to come and explain to me in detail what exactly my daily routine would involve.

The day started with a 5:00 am wake up bell ring. Within thirty minutes, we'd be expected to get ready to start the day, be dressed and ready to head to the conference hall for our 5:30 am *'sabha'*—a daily dose of meditation, light yoga, and breathing exercises. By 7:00 am we'd be let go and required to go to the nurse's station to get our daily glass of morning *Panchgavya*.

Panchgavya was the main component of the cow therapy treatment. As described to us via a live demonstration during our morning session—the drink was made of five ingredients—*desi* cow milk, *desi* cow yogurt, *desi* cow *ghee*, *desi* cow *gaumutra* and *desi* cow *gobar*. The drink mixed together these five items and the result was a green, rather grassy drink. We were to drink a full glass in the morning on an empty stomach.

As we attempted to keep down the drink and do that with a smile (or at least that was my strategy), the other hospital nurses would wheel their way to each room with the medicine cart and distribute to us our morning medicines. For me this turned out to be about twelve Ayurvedic pills and two syrup solutions. These medications were to be had after our breakfast.

Generally we'd be expected to shower and get dressed (if not already at 5:00 am), then by 8:00 am make our way to the patient's cafeteria to have our breakfast. While there were solar panels to heat the water and the weather outside was ridiculously warm and humid, without hot water, it was quite a challenge. This was for the first time, in my daily routine, that the absence of an attendant proved difficult for me. I ended up taking cold showers as the hot water was only available by bucket from the other side of the campus. I didn't have the strength or the ability to do this myself. I was fortunate that after a few days into my stay, some of the attendants offered to get me a bucket of water. This was also one of the first times I felt compassion—the same kind I was used to in New York at hospitals and by volunteer organizations there.

To say that our breakfast was simple would be an understatement. It was my first indication that the kitchen was also under very strict instructions. It very quickly came to light that our food choices were incredibly selective. To begin with and given the hospital was established by Jains, it followed a strict Jain diet, vegetarian and no root vegetables including potatoes, garlic and onions. Additionally, as I was there during the monsoons, Jains also restrict their diet of several vegetables including cauliflower and green leafy vegetables during this season. The patient's kitchen also followed an organic and macrobiotic regimen, which proved rather challenging due to the climate and the reality that within the Indian agricultural landscape, these products were sparse. However, the hospital was mainly self-contained and the surrounding campus property yielded the food that made its way into our *thalis*.

The restrictions weren't only on vegetables, as a result of the strict guidelines put in place for cancer patients, the hospital also followed a gluten-free diet and only seasonal fruits (namely pomegranates and papaya) were permitted.

After an 8:30 am breakfast time wrap-up, we'd go back to our rooms and take our medicines. We'd then go to the nurse's station and get our bowl of *gobar*. Twice a day we were to apply the *gobar*, they had freshly collected from the *gaushala*, to coat our tumour areas completely and then stand in the sun to permit it to air dry.

Some days this process would take an hour, sometimes more. They had divided the terrace above the hospital into two zones, for men and women to freely apply this in privacy. It was quite literally a cancer locker room in the sky. Without words, we knew where the disease was affecting each individual. I can't say I'll ever get the sight out of my head.

It was a good thing that there were no mirrors there. I think I would not have had the strength to take on this challenge, if I had seen what I looked like, coated in *gobar*. At any rate it is not a pretty picture, but for me, it had been years since I publicly took off my shirt and exposed myself in that manner.

It's a strange thing. I had never sunbathed or really ever felt comfortable at the beach. It was partially because of body image issues (I was always on the heavier side) and also because of the fear of tanning and turning *kala*. Yet here I was, standing partially clothed, looking up at the sky and praying to the Gods to let these *gobar* patches over my tumours work their magic and shrink—something no chemo, radiation or experimental drug was able to do for me.

As the *gobar* dried, I'd head back to my room to wash up. Thankfully by mid-morning the water would be slightly warmer and I'd not need to ask for a bucket of hot water, I could just use the water from the tap in the bathroom. As I would be getting dressed, the sister's *dhol* would beat and it was time for our morning *Ukala* drink—a combination of *neem, tulsi,* turmeric, ginger and cinnamon (along with some other Ayurvedic substances they chose not to share with us). Upon drinking our medicine, we'd have a slight break to just rest and chat with one another. I was always so tired I'd head back to my room and lie down inside the mosquito net (during the daytime it would protect me from the countless flies and mosquitos).

Just as I'd try to sleep, lunch would be ready. I'd make my way to the cafeteria towards the end part of the half hour time slot they'd given us and wait for an empty chair. The majority of the patients sat on the floor. As a result of my back, I found it challenging to sit on the ground, so I waited for space on one of the two benches that housed individuals with similar problems.

Lunch was always the same—*roti, dal, subzi* and rice—a typical *thali* meal, but far from a typical *thali* taste. The *rotis* were made of oats. The only *dal* served was *moong dal*. Only three vegetables were used—*lauki, parval* and *karela*. Finally, the rice was the untreated red rice variety. Of course everything was prepared in either mustard oil or *desi ghee*. I can't say the food was intolerable, but it was a challenge. After years of chemotherapy where everything tasted like nails and sawdust, I took it as a bonus to have food with some form of actual taste and made myself a promise that everything I ate—I'd eat with a smile—no matter what.

It's a strange feeling. I remember what it felt like sitting in the individual chemo stations at the hospital. For the most part, we had curtains separating us from other patients, but every time the curtain opened we'd glimpse into each other's miseries. Now just a few months later, to be sitting in such close proximity to other patients and accepting that food— our meals were going to be my new chemotherapy—I never expected the reactions to so closely emulate that of the hospital.

There were the usual whiners, complainers, wise-asses, numerous patients disobeying orders and finally countless patients simply refusing treatment. As I looked to the left and then looked to the right, the kitchen staff came around with stainless steel containers plopping our trays with food. While I can't attest for having ever had food in a prison, based on every film and television program I've seen, our setup was fairly similar. The only difference was probably that we had top grade food given to us, but its presentation and the looks on everyone's faces matched perfectly with a prison cafeteria.

And ultimately we were in jail. The room next to us housed the area for caregivers. While their meals comprised of wheat and sugar and different pulses and vegetables, we were on a strict diet and I knew with my chemo attained heightened sense of smell—there was also medicine mixed into our meals.

The last time I remember seeing a grown man cry and not be willing to eat food, was when I was visiting Mom at the rehab centre post her craniotomy surgery. While she was learning to live without her peripheral vision and adjust to a life where doing basic chores would be framed within a limited visual reality, the neighbouring bed had a stroke patient relearning how to eat. He pained his way bite after bite as tears rolled down his face, it was clear he was struggling to actually utilize his muscles in order to chew.

While that vision had remained forever etched in my head, I saw this recently diagnosed patient beside me, simply look at his food and begin to cry. He was completely able, in fact his digestive system was completely intact, but he simply didn't like what the food looked like and upon barely taking a first taste found it inedible. I on the other hand, simply appreciative of the effort put into making the food and knowing the purpose behind my stay, took each bite and counted my blessings. As the man's tears turned his *rotis* soggy, I wondered about my willpower. It's a strange thing that while the world I existed in in that moment was so foreign to me—why was I willing to accept it and him not?

I didn't have to think much as I got my answer with what I noticed on the other side of myself. I found a young woman laughing, reacting outwardly the same way I was feeling inside. She looked at me and stated *'kitna tasty khana hai na'*. I laughed and replied *'bahut'*. While the crying man remained unamused, we ate the remainder of our meal in sync and in a state of joy. By our last bite we'd become friends. Her name was Monali, she was from Jabalpur and was undergoing treatment for breast cancer. In her early thirties, she had a seven-year-old daughter; her zest for life and all this ridiculousness was infectious. As we stood to put our plates in the dirty dishes bin we saw a young man come prancing into the cafeteria in a T-shirt and panama pants. He couldn't be older than twenty five, I thought.

Monali and I decided to sit ourselves back again and give the young man company. His name was Rajeev and it turned out he was only twenty one. He was fighting an aggressive gastric cancer diagnosis. As his mother hovered above him and started to recite their never-ending journey from Assam to Gujarat—I imagined for a quick moment Mom and I—had she been there for me at this stage in my cancer battle.

It instantaneously struck me again how alone I really was. Seeing the bevy of support that surrounded me for each patient—I felt this sense of true isolation. It didn't help matters that every person there who wished to speak to me, their first question was, 'who's your attendant?' Of course, I'd say I didn't have one and the next logical question was then where were my parents. I'd then politely reply that they had passed away. Of course then curiosity would get the best of them seeing my relatively young age. The question then would be—how? I never thought I'd ever have to repeat the same words 'I'm alone and my parents are dead' as many times in such a short span of time in my life. Of course, I also never thought I'd hear and be referred to as 'the orphan' as many times in quick succession in my life as well.

As we waited for Rajeev to finish his meal, we cheered him on. It was no less than what my friends used to do for me while in the chemo ward. As we'd see the monitor clock down and the IV drip almost come to an end, we'd countdown. Instead of counting down drips, we were counting down bites. Rajeev's mom stood in amazement and seeing her tears turn to a smile both Monali and I also smiled—it was clear that a bond was being tied, not just by cancer but by a joy for life and of the hope we were bringing to each other.

As we exited the cafeteria, we were the last ones out. Monali decided to converse with the 'manager' of the patient's kitchen. She asked what would be served at night. He didn't seem amused but answered rather politely. As we heard him, it felt like he was mistakenly repeating the lunch menu. Monali stopped him to ask just this but he said no, he was reciting the dinner menu. It was nearly identical to our lunch. He added that he'll see us at 5:00 pm and again we looked at each other thinking he was mistaken, but he repeated that the food would be served at 5:00 pm and if we weren't there by 5:30 pm, we would go hungry till the next morning. This was because the hospital practiced *chauviar*, a Jain fasting diet where meals were consumed strictly between sunrise and sunset.

We walked out in slight disbelief, perhaps our fear and nervousness was being overshadowed by the sheer insanity of what we had all signed up for. We laughed as we made our way back to the hospital rooms. It was now time to take our afternoon medicines and catch a short break from the daily routine.

As I returned to my room, my room partners were there. They were from Mumbai. The trustee had ensured that I be given a room with someone that spoke English. The woman Sarangee, in her twenties, was accompanying her cancer-stricken mother who was clearly in a tremendous amount of pain. I asked her how she was doing. It was obvious to me she was beyond unwell. As I started to find out about her case, one of the Ayurvedic doctors came in to assess her. He looked at her, asked a couple of basic questions and then spoke to Sarangee, a conversation which he conveyed very loudly, permitting me to hear everything without any intention of wanting to.

I was a little surprised by what he said. He believed she was faking, that the pain was because she was not eating and a result of her not taking the medicines. He had absolutely no allopathic instruments to measure anything and he suggested that she just continue the course and take the Ayurvedic pills for her pain (keeping in mind that they will take time to kick in but they will... eventually). Sarangee wished to garner more assessment but the doctor seemed unwilling to break protocol and then accused Sarangee of coming ill-prepared, as in that she should have brought painkillers along if her mother needed it as they were not able to prescribe nor would they endorse its use.

As he left in a rather rude rush, I couldn't contain my thoughts and spoke my mind to Sarangee. I told her that

67

her mother was far more ill than these doctors were able to see. As someone who had now seen, far too many times, what end of life looks like—I knew the face of impending death. The sounds (the rattles rather) and breathing of her mom matched something that had become far too familiar for me, I almost felt like the death whisperer. I didn't want to accurately predict the end for anyone yet I also knew this hospital, these doctors, and this isolated world where Sarangee and her mother knew no one else—it was not the right place to end her story. I pleaded they go to a hospital and if possible they leave to return to Mumbai.

It was a strange moment for me. In literally my first day at the hospital, I had gone from a patient to a doctor, something my years of experience with fighting this disease myself and serving as a caregiver had taught me. As the day progressed it was clear that the knowledge I had of allopathy and the lack of knowledge many others had of it, was going to be the greatest gift I could give my fellow patients. In a way I could give back something and make myself feel worthwhile as I stayed there.

Just as I thought I could rest, the security guard made a swoop of the rooms to call us in for the afternoon *sabha*. As we all made our way into the rather humid room with fans barely giving a breeze, there on the small stage platform sat a tiny young woman dressed in a white *salwar kameez*. Automatically seeing a woman interested me as throughout the day, the hospital had felt like an old boy's club except for the nurses. Her name was Fatima Didi and she was the hospital's on-staff spiritual adviser and healer, who would be the primary speaker during our afternoon lectures. She spoke of the disease, then of acceptance and the realities of cancer (the three d's—death, dying and dealing).

It was clear that many individuals were tuned out. Others had difficulty concentrating (due to language barriers as many of the patients only spoke their specific regional language). Thankfully her communication was somewhere between Hindi, Gujarati and English, all three of which I could at least understand, so I benefited from her tough love with compassion approach. Her session concluded with a meditation. I generally have a hard time concentrating when around so many others, but there was something about her energy that I felt was directly targeting me (it is possible since practically all patients were seated on the floor and I was sitting on a plastic chair so I was directly in her view). What I found was that the twenty minutes she requested of us flew by and all the exhaustion and tiredness I had felt prior to the session was nearly gone. We did an '*Om ka jaap*', basically reciting '*Om*' with each breath but breaking the one syllable word into three specific parts for our mouths to enunciate and breathe in with complete concentration over the course of time. It was an interesting sight to see all of us, patients and caregivers alike doing this. It was the first time all day that there was silence and no display of criticism, pain or discomfort from any of us.

I knew that I'd need to reach out and meet Fatima Didi when the chance arose, perhaps make her my new 'Guruji' while at the hospital. As the session concluded, we were treated to our afternoon drink, normally some seasonal cold soup or warm substitute for tea. We'd then be on our way to doing our second gobar coating for the day. Some of us also had a prescription for taking *gobar* baths. This was generally for patients with blood cancer and/or metastasized cancer spread through numerous organs. Literally an entire bathtub was filled with *gobar* and then we were to lay in it for an hour. I too was to get this treatment but without an attendant it was impossible to transport so many buckets, so I went to the doctor's office and they in turn suggested I get a medicated *panchkarma* massage that I happily agreed with compared to the *gobar* bath.

Finishing my second *gobar* coating in the mid-afternoon, would result in a trip back to the bathroom to get cleaned up and by now it'd be time to get ready for dinner. Monali and Rajeev came to my room and we walked the hospital floors like we'd known each other for years. We waited till the tail end when almost everyone had finished their meals to sit down and ate a freshly cooked dinner that mirrored our lunch in taste, smell, looks and every other which way. Still we accepted and we pretended we were eating foods of our choice and simply visualized what we craved for with what we had—this got us through that first dinner. It would end up being our method of getting through the next ten days that lay ahead too, in that cafeteria.

After dinner, we'd take a stroll and then head back to our rooms, to wait for the nurse's to come by and give us our evening medicines. This would be the second time in the day that we'd have a slight break. I ended up staying in Rajeev's room and we shared our war stories with one another. It was clear to me that we were both fighting a losing battle. While I knew my chances, they were living with a false sense of security. Guided by hope and missing the reality, his probability for survival was slim.

Before our conversation could get heavier, the hospital's manager or 'Hospital Dadaji' as everyone called him, made his way door to door with a loud whistle, instructing us to make our way to the conference hall one more time.

The program would begin at sharp 7:00 pm he informed us. As we all hesitantly made our way to the great room, it was clear that patients and caregivers alike were exhausted.

'Hospital Dadaji' began by reciting certain passages from Jain books before starting to sing Jain devotional songs and *bhajans*. He'd try to get us to join in, but it was clear a large number of patients were not Jain, did not understand Gujarati and were simply there for the mandatory attendance.

Thankfully by 7:45 pm 'Hospital Dadaji' opted to stop his horrid singing (as a singer, I was less bothered by the music and more irritated by his terribly nasal and out-of-tune singing voice) and would literally pass the microphone to us to sing our favourite *bhajans*.

Rajeev and I were seated together as the conference was split down the middle and while no one said anything, it seemed to be the rule of the space that women sat on one side and men on the other. We saw Monali front and centre on the women's side. She had been outspoken since the moment she arrived and 'Hospital Dadaji' asked her to sing first. Not being shy for a moment, she readily agreed. As it turned out, Monali had a beautiful singing voice and all of a sudden, the energy in the room took one huge step up. Many other patients and caregivers followed Monali and the night turned from tolerable to enjoyable. At close to 8:40 pm 'Hospital Dadaji' concluded the evening and we were told to go down to the Nurse's station for our final medicine of the day—a glass of *desi* cow milk with a spoon of *desi* cow *Panchgavya ghee*.

By 9:00 pm, we were all asked to make our way to our rooms and call it a night. I remember that night, it was extremely humid and there was no sight of wind in the air. The fans barely brought relief and inside the mosquito net,

71

I felt like I was sweating buckets. As day one of my treatment was coming to an end, I heard a whistle. It was the watchman closing the lights outside and escorting the straggling caregivers chatting on cell phones to make their way into their rooms and close the lights.

I never went to boarding school. I never joined the military. But for the first time in my life I felt like I was living a disciplined life where no excuse would work, I would be accountable for everything and I wouldn't be able to get away with not doing as told. For someone who was so used to being in complete control of his life to now find himself in a total military state, call it opposites attract but I liked it. Perhaps after a long time, I didn't have to worry. I was in a place where I didn't have to plan every moment of my life. I didn't need to constantly be thinking about what to eat, how to prepare it—when to take what, how to spend my time. The hospital allowed me to let go of making decisions. The only decision I needed to make was if I was going to accept what was in front of me and if so, was I going to do that with a smile.

From starting the day, feeling like no one was there for me and how would I be able to survive the hospital without a caregiver, to now already having friends and a support network to spend this time and also finding an avenue to giving back, as I answered the phone and spoke to Deena relaying her the details of my day I realized—I was going to be okay.

CHAPTER 8

Doctor Who?

And if you were to ask me
After all that we've been through
Still believe in magic
Oh yes I do
Oh yes I do
['Magic' by Coldplay]

It's a strange thing to realize, that you may have the answer to someone else's medical needs. I had spent so many years acquiring all kinds of information for myself, Mom and looking back even for Dad, that I guess it shouldn't have come as a surprise that my knowledge about medicine, drugs, treatment, diagnoses, prognoses, hospital routines, costing, side effects etc., had become so natural and engrained in my head that I had literally become a walking encyclopaedia of information.

At the hospital it was clear that this was probably my strongest asset. For other patients and caregivers to see how focused and driven I was with my health and how my knowledge supplanted all medical decisions, it was the kind of vindication I probably had hoped my family would have recognized, rather than doubt my self advocacy. While this can stem from love, there is also a level of trust that one must feel. It's ironic that despite their faith in my intelligence, they always doubted my knowledge.

73

I realized this was all in my head. Ultimately any one with true emotions and feelings, would have stepped in and not let me spearhead my own treatment or that of my mother's, if they felt what I was doing was wrong. Of course, saying I am wrong means that they'd then have to get involved and ultimately no one wanted or wished to be involved outside of asking and being a distant support.

It's funny how this very same sentiment was echoed with patient after patient that I met at the hospital. It was another element that I got to carry from the United States to India. Mom and I witnessed this first hand while she was a patient and we spent a good chunk of her cancer-portioned life living around other patients. We got to see families of all kinds—mothers & daughters, husbands & wives, sisters, friends—there was no relationship that was not represented. Yet for every patient and caregiver, there was someone that should have been there and wasn't and someone that wasn't supposed to be there but was. It's a simple truth that we don't necessarily know who will step up and be there for us and perhaps that's what a real blessing is—that even when we are disappointed by our expectations, our expectations still manage to get met, if we are with good fortune.

I knew I was blessed in this department and perhaps my experience was now offering me the opportunity to fill in a void for families and patients that even they didn't know was missing.

From the day I checked-in to the hospital, there were so many patients I met with such eclectic and varied medical histories, yet the majority of them were of the mind-set that cancer killed and that these efforts we were making at the hospital were a definitive 'cure'. It was challenging for me to hear patients and caregivers talk with such certainty, when I knew that the majority of their knowledge was coming from whatever a doctor had told them.

This unravelled that first night itself. Just as I was giving my day's rundown to Deena on the phone, Sarangee's mother's condition was worsening. As Deena hung up the phone telling me that they will be making calls and figuring out the caregiver issue in Mumbai over the next day and for me to sit tight, I was witnessing the woman in front of me on her last leg of life. Sarangee frantically tried to figure out the next step. Ultimately she took my words to heart and spoke to her family in Mumbai to come get them. In the interim, she made arrangements for her mom to go to an allopathic hospital several kilometres away, in an attempt to reduce her ever-worsening pain.

She quickly packed their things and left the hospital and my first night turned from peaceful and safe to chaotic in an all too familiar setting in India. I ultimately went to bed in the room alone. Sarangee and I exchanged numbers, I planned to check in with her, hoping her mom would make the journey to Mumbai safely and get to close her eyes with all of her family around her in familiar surroundings.

It was tough to end my day with a smile and a laugh upon witnessing this moment. But I found solace in the fact that I was there to comfort Sarangee, at what was likely the most challenging chapter with her mother. It was also a tell-tale sign that something that had started in the US was also developing here in India—relationships with strangers. Time was not going to be the determinant of the value and intensity of a friendship.

By the time I woke up the next morning, this was further brought home by the fact that Rajeev and his mother came over to meet me prior to the *sabha* with some fruit and to check in on me. As I detailed the late night happenings with Sarangee and her mom, they seemed alarmed. Rajeev seemed particularly disturbed by the news. As his mother went back to the room, he and I spoke for some time about the disease.

He found in me a friend, a brother, an older more experienced patient in whom he could confide and talk about the fears, the realities and the sadness he felt for his family. As his questions were mainly on the morbid end, I chose to answer him honestly rather than sugar-coat things. I could tell that the more I shared, the more at ease he was. So often we try to protect those we love by shielding them of the reality. At the end of the day, the truth is what provides any cancer patient an opportunity to have control of their life. For Rajeev, hearing the details both good and bad, of his disease provided him an insight and a will to fight from a real place. When you actually know the odds, you are likely to work that much harder to win.

As I saw Rajeev, I was taken back to my initial months as a patient. I longed to have someone tell me the reality. Sure I had the internet and the ear of my doctors (thankfully) to give me my reality check but I didn't have a real presence in my life to share my fears, doubts, insecurities and openly discuss my journey. I had Mom there every step as an inspiration. Yet I had to protect her from anything but a happy ending. Only once she got sick, did we both find support systems of other patients and caregivers that permitted us to finally feel at home and have a sense of community.

For Rajeev, I became the first support he had to actually grasp his disease. For me, he was a younger version of myself following a medical path I had taken and ultimately not succeeded at. For both of us, the time at the hospital became that much more important. As his mom returned, we headed to the conference hall for our morning session. I could see Monali already seated in the front with eyes closed meditating. We were late and attempted to join the rest. It took me a minute to settle down and feel ready to start the day. I took a deep breath and what seemingly used to be an impossible task, of sitting in a group and going into a meditative state, became a natural process.

As we opened our eyes and looked up, there was another man seated next to the doctor who had been leading the session. Dressed in a white *kurta pajama* with a shawl draped over, he was introduced to us as Romeshbhai. Like Fatima Didi, he was someone who offered his time to work with patients and caregivers teaching them about meditation and yoga. With his *Jai Gurudev* proclamation, it was clear that he was a follower of Sri Sri Ravi Shankar. I was not familiar with him other than having read about the Art of Living program.

Romeshbhai then took our meditation one step further and actually showcased specific *pranayama's*. I was familiar with certain types but never really focused with the intensity I should perhaps have been doing. Of course over the past several months as I developed certain breathing issues, I had an easy excuse. But thanks to a successful one month of *kunjal kriya*, I was feeling lighter and my breathing was far more regular. From alternate nostril breathing to breath retention to equal breathing to bee breath—I explored the various *pranayama's* that morning. I appreciated the energy with which he shared these techniques with us.

While I wasn't sure what benefit they'd have for me, I kept an open mind and managed to successfully participate for nearly one hour of breathing exercises. As the session ended and I went for my second day's glass of *Panchgavya*, I felt a level of energy I wasn't quite sure how to explain, but I was certainly better than I had felt in some time.

As I walked to my room, I saw Umeshbhai there, checking in on me. He had been made aware of Sarangee's mom and I chose not to offer my thoughts as I knew I was already a concern for him.

He assured me that they'd find a suitable match for my room and then he asked if I had any updates about caregivers. I told him that I had spoken to Deena and they were working on it. He then walked me towards the other side of the building. He showed me the *gaushala* at the back of the campus. He suggested I take a visit there once or twice a day. He went on to suggest I go to 'Hospital Dadaji's' office and purchase coupons to feed the cows. Feeding the cows by hand with jaggery and giving the cows the option to lick directly off our hand provided blessings. Apparently if they licked the lifeline on the hand, it was meant to extend our life. Normally, I wouldn't have taken his words very seriously but the belief that I saw in his eyes was truly convincing.

I spoke to Rajeev and Monali as they were headed to breakfast about the *gaushala* and they agreed to join me later in the day to visit the cows.

And with that, a routine developed. We made our way to the cafeteria and had our sans-surprise breakfast. That followed with taking our medicines, my *gobar* coating, cleaning bath and morning *Ukala*. Rajeev, Monali and a couple of other patients then gathered and we walked our way to the *gaushala*. With 25 Rupees receipts for feeding the cows, we walked towards the entrance where one of the labourers took our tickets and started to fill individual buckets with the food to feed the cows.

I instantly noticed how quiet and calm the *gaushala* was. There was only one noise, it was a mantra playing from the megaphone and not to my surprise—it was the *Navkar Mantra*. The caretaker informed me that the mantra played 24/7 and the *gaushala* at present housed over 200 Gir breed *desi* cows.

My knowledge about different cows and *desi* breeds was next to nothing. Upon doing my research for the hospital, I had discovered that the Indian cow was now a rarity as during the fifties and sixties many of the cows were crossbred with imported bulls and semen. As a result, the various *desi* cows that had once inhabited the many villages of India were now being replaced with Jersey cows and crossbreeds. The purity of the *desi* cows, different breeds suited for different climates, was never challenged. From its place in mythology, culture and society, I was always aware of the cow's holy place in India. But this *gaushala* and my newly acquired knowledge about cows offered me a first-hand experience, adding to that, coming face to face for the first time with my medicine—it was quite overwhelming.

As we walked into the *gaushala* with food in hand, I expected a swarm of cows to make their way towards us but instead they stayed in their individual places. Unlike the experiences I had had in the city seeing cows and bulls charge my way when with food in hand, these cows were something truly different—something truly special.

As I made my way to a couple of the cows, they stared at me. I stared back. There was no fear on either side. I petted the side of the cows and slowly made my way towards their front taking a piece of the jaggery-coated food and gently feeding one of them. I resisted leaving my hand there for the cow to lick and retreated back. Monali was beaming as she raised her hand and proclaimed she had got her blessings. I walked over to her and asked her to show me exactly how to leave my hand, so as to get the cow to lick my palm. We did a practice trial and then we went to another cow and I fed her. This time resisting moving my hand away, I let her lick the gooey jaggery off my palm. She did just that. It felt weird, almost ticklish.

The moment brought an instant smile to me as well. But something more significant happened. The palm, the same palm that for so many months had lost any real feeling or sensation, felt alive again. One cow's lick wasn't magic, but I felt that my hand was alive again. I was instantly hooked. Monali and I agreed that we'd come to the *gaushala* twice a day, in the morning and then again in the afternoon for the remainder of our stay.

As I saw Rajeev and his mom along with other patients and caregivers making their way through the *gaushala*, the words that Umeshbhai had shared with me from the morning resonated so strongly. He had said that this was the ultimate thanks we can give to the cows for giving us so much. In one instant—I was no longer an outsider trying to understand a culture, a religion or an animal—I was having a direct connection.

I was part of a full circle, feeding the cows and in turn the cows giving me their medicine and thus giving me more time to feed them again. I'd never felt so close to an animal before, having never had pets this was so much more. I understood why that poster in the doctor's office had the cow goddess Kamdhenu and why the cows were being referred to as *Gaumata*. Just as they fed their offspring, they were nourishing us—giving us a fighting chance as well.

When I got back to my room I was feeling a sense of belonging—something I had been longing for. But it wasn't my connection with Rajeev or Monali but rather my connection to the land and the cows that occupied my mind. That afternoon after lunch and medicine, rather than resting I decided to walk the campus. I started to explore and learn more about all the trees and plants scattered throughout the property, all used for the medicines and food we were being given. Suddenly I was the New Yorker I had loved being, exploring my surroundings and along the way discovering new things.

While most of the patients and caregivers were blindly following the routine that was being given to us, I wanted to learn why we were being given certain things and why some things were off limits. I knew I'd have the *gaushala* routine each day but now I wanted my routine to involve learning about all aspects of the treatment.

I thankfully found a resource for information with Dr. Balsara, a doctor in biotechnology & botany who focused his time there on cancer research. Meeting him I got to actually understand why we were taking what was being prescribed for us. He was the man behind the medicine. It was an added bonus that he could also translate the many things I couldn't read in Gujarati into English. With him, I explored the compound and he became a voice of reason for me. Open to debate, hence giving me one intellectual to discuss my health and the treatment with without having to follow blindly, something I was simply not used to nor willing to comply with while staying there.

For the first time since coming to India I felt like I had met someone who knew something more about my illness and health in general than I did. Simply knowing that someone was there to provide a legitimate experienced voice further enhanced my faith.

It was a good day. By dinner time when Monali, Rajeev and I convened, I felt altogether like a different person.

Monali approached me with her roommate's medical paperwork. She requested I take a look and give the patient some recommendations as they were concluding their eleven day stay and weren't sure what the next best option would be for them.

It was only day two, but I felt a sense of being needed and now between the *gaushala* and meeting Dr. Balsara I felt like my learning and understanding was on the right track. I felt in the right frame of mind to offer guidance and also pass along some faith with it.

My euphoria was short-lived though as I checked my mobile phone and saw that Sarangee had replied to my morning SMS with the news that her mother had indeed passed away. It was fitting in a way that as I was helping another patient, my accurate prediction of what was going to happen with Sarangee's mother came true. It also gave me the courage to speak my mind with other patients. As much as I was becoming a believer—I was not going to stop seeking answers. It was important for me to make sure each patient there was getting as much information about their disease, condition and options. Not everyone there had the same privileged background that I did and it was my goal to be there as a support, if and when it was required.

While I knew I needed to care of myself, I also knew that being there for others was going to be part of my treatment. It was something I was suffering great withdrawal from, after the long time I had spent caring directly and indirectly for Mom. Being in a place where I could voice my thoughts and actually have others listen— suddenly I had the power to make a difference.

That night after dinner and before *bhajan* time, Monali and I were talking about choices. As I shared with her in detail my journey, she stopped me and asked why I simply never gave up. The truth was that I had thought about it. While Mom was still alive, I simply couldn't muster the courage to leave her alone. Since she had died, it had crossed my mind quite often but perhaps I still feared death. Despite my claims that I was ready to die at any point in time, I was living a life of self-preservation. I prepared for my death but I was unwilling to die.

Perhaps because of that unwillingness, I had ended up at the hospital. While I still had many days to figure things out, Monali was the first person after the Shahs to offer me a place to stay. She suggested I come to Jabalpur with her and the two of us could do the treatment together. I still didn't know what was in store for me, but it was a sincere invitation that meant the world to me. Time and time again, other patients and caregivers who opened up their hearts and their homes to me, gave me a sense of home and blessed my life. I started to sing the song 'Home 'by Simply Red. It was one of Mom's favourite songs. Not sure how and why it came out but it did. Monali overheard me singing and quickly realized that I sang as well.

She asked me why I didn't sing in the evening *sabha*, I told her I didn't know religious or devotional songs. If I did, I only knew one or two lines, that's it. Little did I know, this random performance would result in 'Hospital Dadaji' calling me to the stage later that evening during the *sabha*, Monali had apparently told him that I wanted to sing.

I was of course mortified. I hadn't really sung in many years. I loved to sing. Mom once told me I started to sing even before I learnt to speak. I remember taking blank cassettes and recording my voice, singing popular English and even Bollywood songs. My passion continued all through school, through choirs, musicals and bands as an adult. However with my cancer diagnosis, it seemed to have also taken my voice with it.

Perhaps it was the medicine, may be it was my emotional state or likely a combination of the two, since cancer had struck, and I had lost my singing voice. Going up on stage and singing that night felt like a first audition. While I knew it was just patients and caregivers and one terrible-singer in 'Hospital Dadaji', I simply wasn't ready. But he didn't take no for an answer. Of course, I had nothing to sing. He suggested I sing anything, jokingly telling me even singing the ABCs would be fine.

Being there, in that moment, one song struck me. As an avid fan of Bollywood, there was a song I remembered. I also realized I could quickly look up the lyrics online and sing from my phone. Nervously I grabbed the microphone from 'Hospital Dadaji' and began to sing the title song from 'Kal Ho Na Ho'. The lyrics seemed to instantly resonate with everyone. Somewhere between the first and second line of the song, I felt a change. The shaky, slightly fearful voice became more assured and more in tune. It wasn't the voice I once had, but it was a voice with an emotional depth from years of experience that came pouring out.

As I sang I saw that there was not a single dry eye in the hall. I had to thank Monali and 'Hospital Dadaji' for giving me the push to do something I loved again. This wasn't karaoke where I wouldn't be judged, this was a test and I had passed. 'Hospital Dadaji' was in shock for he realized that despite my American accent and American ways—I was at heart very Indian. I could see the inspiration in other patient's eyes too and I knew it wasn't just because I was reading medical records or that I had travelled the farthest to be there for treatment. I was connecting with them on a deeper level. 'Hospital Dadaji' warned me that from that night onwards, I'd be a daily performer at *bhajan* time. Unlike just a few minutes before that, I was ready and willing.

As the night loomed, I returned to my room still left unoccupied by any other patient. Deena had left a missed call and I called her back. She mentioned that Sapna Massi had physically gone to Bhavna Massi's home (the one who passed away years back) to meet her sons. She had pleaded with these cousins of mine to take turns to come and spend time with me at the hospital. Apparently even after the chat, no one was necessarily volunteering to come so Deena was trying to find out if I had suggestions as to how to organize them coming and what my needs were. I was very frank with her and upon hearing that Sapna Massi was literally left in the same position as she was prior to my coming to the hospital, I was simply unwilling to let anyone else suffer for me. I flatly told Deena to stop the search and conversations with others. I was going to be fine on my own. While she seemed concerned, I told her that I had a wonderful support system of patients and caregivers who were stepping in and I had faith that I'd be able to do it on my own.

Deena was more concerned about Umeshbhai's reaction, given that he was expecting someone to arrive. I suggested that I would tell him that it's happening but in a few more days. By then if there were no issues, they'd be more confident in my being able to stay alone without an attendant. I also suggested to Deena that I'd talk to 'Hospital Dadaji' about having another roommate, perhaps that would also alleviate some of their concerns.

And with that conversation, I had let go. I wasn't going to let those who weren't there affect my time at the hospital from focusing on my health. I wanted to heal and that too without any additional feeling of guilt for taking up someone else's time away from their life. I was happy and unlike the night before, I fell asleep with great optimism, feeling a sense of change for the better.

CHAPTER 9

Back To Black

All alone
Without you here
How long have I gone
Feels like time stands still
I keep counting the days
Just to try and find a way
To come back home
['You' by Shaznay Lewis]

By day three, I felt like my daily routine was coming into full form. I'd wake up at 4:55 am, just a few minutes before the bell rang and go for a bath. By 5:30 am, I was ready in the conference hall for the meditation session. I wasn't particularly fond of the doctor but thankfully most of my days there I got to see Romeshbhai.

He and I had developed a connection thanks to Fatima Didi who took an interest in me. After my daily morning *gobar* process and visit to the *gaushala*, I'd meet her in the conference hall. She had 'office hours' of sorts where she offered energy healing, one on one meditation, crystal therapy treatment and some conversational spiritual counselling. She knew I was on my own unique journey. I shared with her several articles I had written about the loss of my mother and the many shades of grief. She was drawn by my sincerity and willingness to share.

Together the one-two punch of Romeshbhai and Fatima Didi proved to be an amazing setup for the spiritual journey I was clearly on. Through the various *pranayama's* and therapies, I was focusing on myself in a way that I had been unable to in the US. Perhaps without the day to day tensions of work, preparing meals, keeping friends informed of my status and maintaining a positive attitude—I was actually able to look inside and get a greater sense of peace and understanding of my isolation.

I was actually beginning to understand that all the hurt, the pain, the grief, the guilt—I was carrying far too much. I had been saying that I had let go, I had passively stated it but not found a vehicle to actually actively let go. Between meditation and yoga, I was finding a way to make that happen. What was surprising was that it wasn't something I was being taught—it was just happening naturally.

I think for the first time in a long time, I was feeling safe and secure to be one with myself. The thoughts, the pressures, the questions were all gone and I could just focus on my inner connection. The *Navkar Mantra* became automatic, it wasn't something that now required effort, it brought me security and it didn't have to be at a set time.

I was lucky that in my first few days, the hospital was still housing the Jain *sadhus*. My afternoon time at the *gaushala* then had led to a daily afternoon walk around the campus. On Day three it landed me directly at the *apasra*. While I had seen the *sadhus* the first two days, I wasn't sure what to say to them. But that day I was ready to speak to them. As I knew they were the same sect as my family, I went in and asked if I could sit with them. They smiled and let me sit there. I began to share some things about myself. As I tried to feel a connection, I noticed how fixed they were on asking questions. I wasn't sure what I expected by sitting with them but for all the time that I was beginning to spend with myself—I was feeling a sense of disconnect.

Still, I had a purpose for being there. Since arriving in India, there was one question that lingered in my mind, it was something I had asked all of them. Thus far, I had yet to get a satisfactory answer.

I asked the *sadhus* about *karma* and suffering. Over the years I had heard so many tell Mom and me that everything we endured was a result of our *karma*. Additionally, the journey we were on, both individually and together, was a form of suffering. What I didn't understand was how anyone got to define someone else's experience as suffering? Mom and I had made a pact to live life happily no matter what. If we accepted all the 'suffering' that was coming our way with a smile and laughter—is that really suffering? And if *karma* was really the determinant of our lives, if we managed to survive through the suffering— wouldn't that mean that we were closer to *nirvana*?

As I asked the *sadhus*, I got textbook answers. It was basically everything I had heard before, there was nothing of substance that I could latch onto through our conversation. What was interesting to me was how connected the *sadhus* seemed to be to the world. As isolated as I felt, I realized that the life and path that I was on was perhaps even more isolated than that of the *sadhus*. It was the first time I wondered if the *sadhu* life was my missed calling in life.

I left the *apsara* and met with Rajeev and Monali as it was just before dinnertime. As they both shared some personal thoughts about their lives and the fears that they carried about their illness and their families, I just didn't understand how the *sadhus* could be so blasé about the questions I had. It was almost as though they had no opinion of their own. Perhaps my time with them was a reminder for me to not let go of all attachments.

As I spent time with myself that evening post dinner, taking another walk alone, I thought about my place in the world. Would I really be missed if I never came back from the hospital? I had already said so many farewells in the US, that most of my friends had already accepted the fact that they may never see me again. For my family despite my pleas for help, they too had said their hellos and goodbyes upon my first weeks in India. So ultimately for whom was I fighting so hard and why?

I guess I knew the answer but I didn't want to admit it. I was doing everything—for myself. Call it self-preservation or narcissism; I was unwilling to follow the road that had been paved for me. As I tried to rationalize this selfish behaviour, I realized that I had actually walked over 20 laps around the campus. The hospital guard asked me if I was okay walking as much as I had.

I told him I was fine, in fact I was feeling better than I had in quite some time. Perhaps it was my mind in thought, my body in sync with the food and the atmosphere or my trips again and again to the front of the *gaushala* to get a peek at the *desi* cows, I noticed a change in my physical energy level. I was always a big walker in New York but I had arrived at the hospital weighing 96 kgs (I had managed to lose a few kilograms since arriving in India). Still it was very unhealthy weight and walking and putting so much pressure on my legs in the past had been highly problematic.

But here, I wasn't even feeling it. Of course, that wasn't the case when I got to bed. I had asked Dr. Balsara about the constant burning sensation I felt at the soles of my feet and he suggested doing a massage with a copper bowl and ghee. I immediately managed to get the ingredients from the nurse's station and started rubbing away. I saw my foot turn pitch black (supposedly this act gets rid of the heat from the body). I noticed that by the time I went to bed, I was feeling a sense of coolness that I hadn't felt throughout the day. Given that our rooms were much warmer than outside, without electricity for much of the night and being used to waking up in a puddle of sweat—this was a relief.

Perhaps the sweaty nights and lack of electricity enabled my morning baths without any requirement of hot water. While the hospital was thoroughly clean, there were many issues with the facility. I started the first couple of days complaining but realized that I needed to simply endure the way things were if I was actually going to focus on the treatment. This was no Club Med and my expectations couldn't be that high. I needed to spend that energy taking advantage of the therapies and treatments offered alongside the daily routine they had set up for me.

As each day passed, old patients finished their time and new patients came in. Monali, Rajeev and I had all thankfully started together, so we knew we'd have each other through the entire duration of our stay, our friendships grew to include several other patients. By Day seven, we had become an entire posse having each meal together, attending *sabhas* and at the *gaushala*. Our time together had also become part of the routine for me. From the early days of going to bed at the instructions of the guard with his whistle, now we ended up meeting in someone's room sitting, sharing, laughing and crying together.

While the hospital's goal was to teach us about what we needed to do at home to continue the treatment we were learning there, it was clear to us that part of our recovery was also having a safe environment where we could slowly adjust into the routine without fear of judgment. As we all started to prepare for our departure from the hospital in the coming days, it all seemed too short.

What seemed like an eternity on day one was now just a few days away from ending. No one really felt different physically as a result of the medicines and food. Some patients had developed diarrhoea from the *Panchgavya* but there were really no side effects to everything our body had been consuming. I personally felt some improvement in the neuropathy issues I had come to the hospital with. I also felt a consistent higher dose of energy than what I had when I first arrived.

The biggest change we all felt, was perhaps the sense of belonging and a heightened sense of spirituality. We had each other, having shared an experience and that too by trying something that we all had some level of trust in but were unsure of the outcome, the hospital created a network for its patients to find peace in one another.

By this point, I was a star at *bhajan* time. Monali and I would duet, I would sing yet another Bollywood song and we could actually see that the same patients who were at first unwilling to even come to the mandatory evening *sabhas* were now looking forward to attending.

I had experienced living in a cancer dorm, when Mom and I had stayed in Hope Lodge in New York City, where she was a patient. My time at Laxmiprasad so strongly resembled my time there in so many ways, it felt like déjà vu. But my time at Hope Lodge ended with my mother's death and on day eight, we witnessed the death of one of the patients at the hospital. It was a welcome reminder that our temporary dorm life was just that—temporary.

I had spoken to Sapna Massi about my time at Laxmiprasad coming to an end. She knew I would return to her home for a couple of days, as I had said once my time at the hospital was over. Then I'd head back to Delhi to in turn go to the US. I wasn't sure how long I'd still be in India, but the past week at the hospital provided a sense of comfort and love that I had not experienced since Mom was alive and we were staying at Hope Lodge.

The last couple of days just flew by. I was so focused on my routine and spending the remaining time with my hospital friends, I was solely focused on the now. As I woke up on my final day, I got up feeling uneasy. It was the first morning that I was unable to meditate. Yet again, I was leaving a place that I had begun to feel was like home.

As Deena called to tell me that she and Massi were nearby, I began to mentally prepare for my return back to civilization and the questions that I was sure were waiting for me.

I checked out at 'Hospital Dadaji's' office and bought a one-months' supply of all the medicines and some of the food to take with me. I must say it was nice to see Deena and Sapna Massi make a second trip to pick me up. After eleven days completely on my own, left to make new friends and survive no matter what the condition or potential risks, to have someone there who knew me prior to the last eleven days was comforting.

As I said goodbye, my Massi saw the tears in the eyes of my new friends. She was surprised by the affection and feelings that so many were conveying after such a relatively short period. As I hugged Rajeev and his mom—something in me knew that I wouldn't see him again. I wasn't sure why I was so pessimistic about his outcome but as I saw his mom give me her blessings, I held onto her and told her that no matter what, you have to have faith.

With Monali, it was a different kind of connection. Our friendship seemed far longer than eleven days, so the goodbye felt that much harder. But there were no tears. We knew we would see each other again. I distinctly remember one of our many chats led to talk of marriage. She told me rather nonchalantly that had she not been married and had a daughter, she would have married me. I felt flattered and could have seen a future with her. Despite our many differences, the way we both saw life was so similar. She and I had developed a way to enjoy life inspite of the many complications that tried to get in the way.

Perhaps that's why I was not happy that she was one of the few there that refused to listen to my medical advice. Monali had an early stage breast cancer diagnosis. She had gone to Mumbai to have a double mastectomy and then subsequently undergo chemotherapy. But prior to the surgery she had a call from an ex-colleague who suggested she come to Laxmiprasad and give naturopathic treatment a try first. That coupled with the fear she saw in her daughter's eyes at the hospital in Mumbai convinced her to try alternative therapy. As she had also shared her medical records with me I was somewhat surprised that she had opted this treatment. For a majority of the patients at the hospital including myself, we were last stage patients. Most were unable to afford allopathic treatment or detected with metastatic cancer so with very limited options, coming here was a last resort. For Monali and some other patients coming to the hospital, it was more a choice between allopathy and alternative treatments.

Monali had made an active choice without even really stepping into the world of allopathy. For the hospital, she was the ideal candidate, as they believed those who have done nothing and start with cow therapy from the start are more likely to fight and beat cancer and more likely to not have the cancer recur. Of course these claims were not based on research or any scientific data so it was simply a leap of faith.

While I tried to advise many patients there about the pitfalls of allopathy, I was also the first to forewarn about blindly trusting any type of doctor or hospital. In Monali's case, I went further, I actually voiced my opinion. I didn't believe she was in the right place. I thought she should have had the surgery and done chemotherapy. Having had many friends with breast cancer, I knew her chances were better than other cancer patients. Still, I had to respect that she was confident enough to believe in the therapy.

After all, despite the whole world literally being available to me for treatment, I was coming there with no choice. Yet she and I treated the hospital, the food and the cows with the same amount of respect. In truth, her faith in the healing power rubbed off on me. Without her, I perhaps would not have been in the same mind-set to taking everything in as I did. Regardless, I knew that my leaving was not the end for us.

I warned her that she needed to keep me in the loop and she needed to be on top of the routine to ensure she doesn't give a reason for the cancer to grow and spread. She assured me that everything we had learnt she'd be able to do at home. She planned to purchase a *desi* cow and gift it to her milkman so as to ensure daily fresh *desi* cow milk, *gaumutra* and *gobar*.

I did take her offer quite seriously to join her in Jabalpur, but I also knew that relying on another patient and that too someone I feared may not be headed in the right direction, was not the best idea for me.

As we drove away from the hospital, I couldn't believe what had transpired in the span of eleven days. I knew I had changed but I wasn't sure if it was enough. I needed more. But how was that going to be possible? Just as I began to chat with Deena and Sapna Massi about my time there the phone rang and it was Umeshbhai. We had just missed each other. I thanked him for the time and efforts of his team to ensure that I was okay. He told me that I must continue treatment no matter what and to not give up hope. He so convincingly stated that everything was going to be alright. That was the difference between the first day and that last day. He had said the same thing on day one and I found it simply to be hodgepodge. As we headed back to Mumbai, somehow I felt there was some truth to what he was saying. But I knew I had a lot to figure out—and I needed solutions not questions.

CHAPTER 10

No Easy Way Out

And everywhere I go
There's always something to remind me
Of another place and time
For love that travelled far and found me
['Remind Me' by Royksopp]

The journey back to Mumbai was an exciting one. I was filled with stories of the wonderful people I had met and the crazy out-of-the-box things I had tried in the name of my health and Ayurveda. Sapna Massi and Deena also seemed optimistic and at least for the ride to my Massi's home, there was a level of accomplishment at their end for helping me on this leg of my journey.

Some say the moment you reach home, reality kicks in and it certainly did for me. Almost immediately upon arriving at my Massi's home, I knew my time there was numbered. Doing any aspect of the treatment that I was told to continue for at least one year, if not two years was not going to sit well with my relatives. I already had only a handful members of my family left, who were willing to help.

My Massi's age and rather outspoken nature was always the thing that drew me to her. But I also saw how that played out within her immediate family. As 'Hum Saath Saath Hain' is how every family attempts to present themselves, the reality is something completely different. My cousin Kushal and I were close from childhood and he had promised me that he'd take me to Shirdi for prayers of Sai Baba, as they were devoted followers, and the previous attempt we had made was cancelled due to an unexpected death in his family. Thankfully now that my time in India had got extended, I would be able to make the journey.

We left bright and early after my morning routine. The trip was rather eventless thanks to my cousin's connections and investment with the Sai Baba temple. We were given VIP treatment. I for one, had heard about this type of Cadillac treatment at holy sites but had never witnessed it first-hand. We met Akhabai, a *hijra* devotee of the temple who escorted us to the waiting area, a rather lovely room, the stadium equivalent of boxed seats.

Within a few minutes, we were whisked away for the *aarti*. While others waited in long queues, we were on the sides and I noticed that our access included being ahead of the barricade. The *aarti* was lovely, albeit rather loud but I could feel the good energy in the overcrowded space. As it concluded, I saw several of the *sadhus* and *maharajis* bow down and touch the feet of Sai Baba, placed there at his tomb site. While most patrons were unable to reach let alone touch them, my VIP status coupled with my cousin informing Akhabai of my medical condition and with us standing just to the side of it, I got the privilege of praying and touching Sai Baba's golden feet.

I left the temple feeling optimistic, believing that anything is possible. As a reminder I chose to buy a ten rupee black thread. While most use these ties as souvenirs, I thought of it as a religious reminder of my open and unwavering faith in life and in the idea that anything is possible.

As we drove back to Mumbai, I noticed the landscape. It was so hard to believe how stark the difference was between the city and the many small villages we passed. Somewhere along the highway, Kushal told me about a *dhaba* that he would always stop at to have food. He spoke of the authentic Maharashtrian style food that was available there. As an obsessed onion and garlic fanatic (ironic given that his parents were staunch Jains who'd go hungry but not have onions or garlic), we stopped there. He was sceptical about my willingness to have food there given the rustic nature of the establishment.

I was surprised by my cousin's choice, mainly because he was someone who travelled the five star hotel restaurant circle, but I also knew that he was a foodie and anywhere that he raved about would be worth a shot. I saw the kitchen and how clean it was despite it being outdoors and literally off the highway. I also saw that everything was made fresh in front of our eyes. I had already been on the no-wheat kick and was surprised to hear that they had *jowar rotis*. It was a name I recognized from the hospital. So many Maharashtrians at the hospital had asked if they were permitted to have *jowar* and the doctors had said it was allowed. I was beyond excited to try this new find.

After countless weeks of no onion, no garlic—I was offered *lasooni methi* with a *jowar roti*. Perhaps it was that my taste buds had been simplified after the hospital and then eating solely at Sapna Massi's place, where they had been adhering to my hospital diet, I felt euphoria in my mouth. The combination was doing just what my cousin had been boasting about since before we even made our way on the trip.

After such a filling meal, yet without breaking any of my diet restrictions, I was daydreaming about the practicality of living in Mumbai and being able to continue my treatment regimen. But the reality of planning this meant that I'd also need to think about my work and sort out my finances. Given that I was in no position to resettle without a stable source of guaranteed income, my family kept harping on how I'd manage between my medical bills and my day-to-day expenses.

I understood their concern but I also knew that the reality of working and continuing such an arduous and time-intensive medical path was next to impossible for me. I needed space to think but I was already living on borrowed time. This unravelled in a rather dramatic manner at Sapna Massi's place. I awoke to loud arguing that the air conditioner could not masquerade. It was the perfect time to focus on the meditation skills I had learned. To my surprise, it provided me the silence I needed to refocus my energy and to not let the noise get to me. Of course the noise was shared with me the next morning when Sapna Massi informed me rather unabashedly that my time with their family was to end. My stay with them was causing friction within the family and as a result of her now forced reliance on her children she couldn't voice her desire to permit me to stay there longer.

She asked me if I had somewhere else to stay in Mumbai. Having already exhausted my choices, I candidly said no. I spoke to Kushal then and asked him for options in terms of getting a place of my own. Frankly the practicality of the situation seemed challenging given my finances and time constraints.

Perhaps as a result of realizing that I was now at the tail end of help being offered and available to me in Mumbai, I thought of returning to Delhi and planning my return back to the United States via the Shah's house. I immediately called them and informed them of my plan to fly back the next day. They did not seem to have a problem except for the fact that their house was fully occupied with visitors and relatives. They offered to send my remaining bags to Jyoti Massi's place (the location of my breathing episode). I was nervous to go there, particularly after their complete lack of interest in my medical journey and the fact that despite my calling every relative upon reaching the hospital, they never called or inquired about my status there.

As I hung up the phone, I felt the lowest I could possibly ever feel. For a change, I was actually on a course of action that I wanted to do, yet there was literally no help; no place; no way for me to continue. As I went to shower I thought about how trapped and helpless I was. I knew I would need to go to a hotel that day and leave Sapna Massi to her peace and her family. I needed to change my flight and then plan accordingly how to get my things in Delhi and fly back to America.

I went to shower and as I soaped my body, my tears overpowered the force of the water. I had been lathering my back and suddenly I felt something unusual. Like any other day, I would wash my back and be able to feel the tumour in my spine when I pushed a specific way against my back fat. That particular day, I noticed that its shape was different. I was not able to push or reach it in the same way. It's almost as though the tumour had shrunk a bit. I was flabbergasted, was this possible? Perhaps it was wishful thinking on my part but in that moment, a moment I really felt could have ended with me walking out of the shower and truly contemplating ending my life—I had received a sign. Perhaps it was my imagination, my desire to find an avenue, a sign from the blessings I felt at Sai Baba's temple or who knows what—my faith was restored. In an instant I saw the right path for me.

I quickly washed up and rushed to Kushal's room. I asked him to book me a cab. I wanted to go back to the hospital. Without hesitation he agreed. I told Sapna Massi that I felt a difference and there is nowhere else for me to go, I can't stop the treatment, it's changing me and giving me a fighting chance, I will go back and do another eleven days. She was worried more about what after those eleven days, I said I'll figure it out but for now I must go. In ninety minutes I had my bags packed and was out the door.

For the second time in less than a month I was making the journey back to the hospital. So much had changed, yet there was one key thing that was different. Even as I travelled alone to the hospital—I was going without doubts. Whether my health would improve or not, I was going towards something and I was going to get better. If nothing else I'd be in a place where I was wanted, where I belonged, somewhere I could think and not be a burden, a responsibility, a liability, an excuse for anyone else.

I called the hospital and lied for the second time telling them I was coming for treatment. I told the trustee that I'd have family joining me but I knew with a hundred percent certainty that no one would visit and I was completely fine with it. I'd have to pay this time and that I was ready to do, as it was a short order compared to what I'd be receiving in return.

It was very fitting that as we left the greater Mumbai area it started to rain, the monsoon had seemingly been delayed that year. I thought about the varied moments of my life since Dad had died, from his cremation to his birthday to when Mom died, rain seemed to always be a constant in the big moments of my life. In many ways, my return to Sevak was a bigger step for me than when I first went to the hospital.

I reached the hospital and for the first time since arriving in India, I breathed a sigh of relief. I felt at home. It's strange that a hospital can feel more inviting and more like home than any other place or being with any other person. As I was warmly greeted by the staff and taken to my room, I knew my life was going to change for the better, no matter where I'd go—I was truly going to be okay.

Perhaps the first sign of what lay ahead was that my phone started having issues upon my arrival. Seemed like some water had gone into the instrument and I was seeing only a partial screen. My electronics were forcing my hand to the act of letting go. Being in an isolated location with limited resources, I slowly began my journey to leaving everything behind and realizing that there was no point in chasing others who willingly chose not to be there. This time was going to be different. I wouldn't call and update the world on my life, I'd just live it and focus on my healing. And with that, I embraced my future.

I arrived at the hospital in the late afternoon. It was impressive how quickly my routine restarted, aware of my specific needs and my discipline, the staff thankfully let me stay in a room by myself while the hospital wasn't at full occupancy. I enjoyed the privacy. It enabled me to stay positive and not feel the absence of a caregiver. Of course I missed Rajeev, Monali and the rest of the gang but I knew a new gang would form—and boy did it ever.

CHAPTER 11

Praying For Time

When love comes calling
Don't look back
When love comes calling
Don't look away

['Don't Look Back' by Telepopmusik]

Given that this was my second stay at the hospital, I was going to make full use of the time and the facilities to create a proper routine for myself. This time it wasn't about trying—this time it was about maintaining. I didn't know if ultimately what I was doing was going to buy me any more time than I actually had, but I knew the quality of my time was going to improve.

Apparently I had left quite a reputation after my first stay and some of the guests that had started just as I left were at the tail end of their eleven days. One such patient was a woman, Ananda, who was accompanied with her daughter Neelam. They were staying in my old room and had been social with my buddies from the last stay. We quickly became friendly because of this. As luck would have it, they had decided to extend their stay by an additional eleven days so I already knew I was going to have good company.

Neelam and I bonded instantly. I saw the devotion and dedication she had for her mom, who despite being in evident pain, was always smiles and laughs. It again mirrored my memories of Mom and me. Neelam's mother quickly turned from Ananda to Ananda Massi for me. Our circle also included a neighbouring local who Neelam and I referred to as Chikli aunty, she was there with her mother-in-law. Then there was a couple from Mumbai, Alpesh uncle and Madhvi aunty. Alpesh uncle was doing the treatment as a just-in-case, after a successful surgery to remove a tumour from his jaw. He had difficulty eating and speaking, but with time, it was expected to recover fully.

While it was a relatively older group than my first hospital batch, they immediately warmed up to me and I to them. In fact, I was given a very old couple as roommates on my second day of the return trip. Within minutes I knew I was going to be helping them more than getting help myself. Almost immediately Madhvi aunty invited me to shift to their room as their last roommates left. I asked the office and they permitted the move.

I didn't realize how having a roommate could enhance my experience. It's an interesting fact to see that sometimes the things we long for come our way without even asking for it. Madhvi aunty had the motherly gene and she cared for me like her own son. She made sure my clothes got washed properly, that I bathed with warm water and ate fruits and other snacks throughout the day. It was a welcome change and again showed me how powerful the kindness of strangers could be.

As I looked for ways to repay the generosity, I got a phone call from Monali who promptly informed me that I didn't need to consciously think about it. In essence, by going through reports, inspiring and showing patients and caregivers that despite my single life, without a family, I was always smiling, happy and accepting what came my way no matter what—I was indeed giving back.

As my routine developed again, I made sure to increase my limits. While the cow therapy remained intact as did the *gobar* treatments, I added some physical movements and exercise to keep my mobility on an upswing. Fatima Didi and Romeshbhai, continued to take time out of their schedules and made sure to personally help me with my spiritual development.

In particular, Fatima Didi was such a powerful force. My back would often pain quite significantly. I always had to sit on a chair but she made inroads towards helping me keep my strength and posture while sitting down. It was a challenge at first but the more time I spent doing meditation, laying down and then having to sit up, I noticed there was a slight shift in my movement, with a sizable change in my pain level.

I wouldn't have believed that stone therapy or energy healing could have such an effect but she and I had a connection that somehow transcended time and space. She shared much of her life with me and I reciprocated in turn altering the dynamics of the relationship to one of mutual appreciation and healing. Call it the years of providing free therapy to my friends but I had developed a good ear and somehow no matter who the other person was, I always ended up having them share their life with me, without much probing from my end.

I think for Fatima Didi to have someone encouraging her abilities and motivating her, was a lot for her to take in. Despite her abilities, she had doubts. She was giving us so much; I wanted to make sure we were giving her something in return. Through this realization I discovered something more about myself. I was much more into my spiritual evolution than I gave myself credit for.

This was apparent nowhere more strongly than, when during the afternoon *sabha* she used me as an example of a patient not willing to give up. It was the first time for me, to hear my own story relayed by someone else, in a manner that championed my decisions and willingness to live by my own rules. I had always thought I was doing things for myself but my acknowledgment of others and my attempts to fend for myself were actually also selfless acts. Perhaps it was the power of hearing things from someone else, especially someone I trusted and hearing that I was not in the wrong with my family, it provided a sense of validation; something I hadn't thought I'd get outside of my friends in the US.

As the days passed my time with Dr. Balsara also increased. My chats with him changed from what to do checklists to understanding the science behind the herb, the plant, the tree and the treatment. It is here that I uncovered that the rigidity with which the hospital administered the medicines and food was not necessarily right as well. While not denouncing the system, I was able to read between the lines that much of the treatment course that I was participating in could be altered in ways to be more convenient to our unique specific conditions.

In my case, I had a sensitive stomach and consuming the *Panchgavya* on a daily basis had begun to create havoc on my system as the monsoons started. Given that the cows were no longer able to go into the jungle regularly to have their greens/meals, the diet they were having was not sitting well with my body. Dr. Balsara suggested I try fresh *gaumutra* instead which I happily switched to, immediately. No doubt the pain and problems I was having stopped.

I was lucky to have Dr. Balsara's ear to bounce things off. I knew most patients and caregivers refrained from speaking to him, thinking he was out of reach. However it was important for me that I learnt from the person who had been so instrumental in my improvement up to this point.

Whatever I learnt during our sessions, I shared with other patients and caregivers, to ensure we had as much information as possible to make the right decisions for ourselves both while at the hospital and ultimately once at home.

For me, this started a longer conversation with Dr. Balsara about the practicality of continuing this entire treatment course in the US. It was a possibility with the herbs and Ayurveda medicines but with the *desi* cow—it was going to be a challenge. Of course then he asked me why I couldn't stay in India till the treatment was complete.

It was a valid question, one that I had started to ask myself, but after a short window in Mumbai I was certain it would be impossible for me to do the treatment in a big city in India, or at least not in Mumbai or Delhi. And even if it was possible, I was not going to get any help from my family.

Dr. Balsara was the first to suggest that I consider staying locally in the area and continue the treatment in the Sevak area itself, with easy access to the hospital and the *gaushala*. It was something that I told him I'd think about, but for the moment I needed to focus on the day-to-day routine at the hospital, that provided some level of relief for me.

I had noticed that I was experiencing a physical transformation. In less than a month since my first admission to the hospital, I had lost almost 6 kgs, I was down to 90 kgs. I wasn't losing the weight quickly but rather quite healthily. It seemed like finally all the weight that I had gained from the years of steroids was finally coming down.

Of course I was always a husky kid and as an adult as healthy as I thought I might have been, I was on the heavier side. Reaching 90 kgs was something I had been at the start of my treatment. When I was first diagnosed, I was 85 kgs. Over the course of the years due to a variety of complications, I progressively got even heavier ballooning all the way to an all-time high of 107 kgs.

What was interesting was that as I saw my weight come down; my energy level was equally going up. As if I was shedding not just weight but the toxins from my body—I was slowly becoming a 2.0 version of myself. The best indication of this change was around my waist. For years I yo-yoed between 38 to 40 inches. For the first time in a long time I noticed that my belt was making its way to the last hole. I hadn't expected my weight to come down while at the hospital but it was a wonderful gift alongside the relief in pain. Of course the weight loss was also contributing to my improved mobility and overall health.

It might sound silly but time flew over the next few days. How my eleven days went by is a mystery. Madhvi aunty, Alpesh uncle, Neelam and Ananda Massi all prepared to leave. I was nowhere near making a decision on what to do next, so I decided to stay back an additional eleven days and pay the fees again (this time the cost increased further).

Thankfully the office permitted me to extend my stay, well aware that I was in need of finding a place to continue the treatment. Also by this point, they were next to certain that no one from my family was going to come and be there with me. I had met with Umeshbhai and he now realized that I could in fact take care of myself but more importantly, nothing should stop me from getting treatment, especially not a family that was content with staying afar.

The longer I stayed, the more I uncovered how many different treatment options and alternative therapies and healers were actually out there. Similar to how I had heard about the hospital through word of mouth, others were privy to a world of 'cures' around the country. As I befriended patients and caregivers from all over India, they offered me suggestions for what to try next if the hospital's course of treatment was not right for me or could only take me so far. It almost seemed like the patients were playing their own cancer version of 'Russian Roulette', hedging their bets on the right formula that would rid them of the disease.

One option I heard, was about a shaman doctor N.R. Narayan Murthy near Shimoga, Karnataka. A farmer and forest expert, Murthy saw patients twice a week and after a one minute consultation or after taking a look at lab reports would offer fifteen to thirty days of treatment free of cost. The medicine would literally be tree stems, roots and barks that he collected from the jungle over the course of the week.

I had actually managed to see a documentary about him, to learn about his magical abilities. He seemed to be a last resort for terminally ill patients and I remember him stating that his main medicine was hope. I was sceptical but again given my new state of always answering with why not, I seriously contemplated making the trip.

My map began to fill up as I heard about additional alternative treatments and plans. From Tibetan medicine in Dharamshala to meeting a *babaji* located about 60 kms from Sevak whose blessings were known to cure patients—I realized that I was perhaps opening myself up to my own version of an alternative cocktail chemotherapy.

But I knew I couldn't just pick up and travel the country by myself with my health being such. In particular given the language barriers and the remote locations of these places, I wasn't sure I'd be able to make it on my own. Additionally, after getting the medicine, I'd need a place to then actually follow the treatment.

The more I thought about it, staying in Sevak and in particular to stay affiliated in some way with the hospital made the most sense for me.

With my second batch of old friends now leaving and meeting yet another group, I knew I now needed to prepare beyond following the daily routine of the hospital. As it happened, I got a call from Monali who told me that she was having difficulty doing her routine at home and had decided to return to the hospital again to do an additional eleven day stay. I was excited that I'd see her again and perhaps we could then seriously think about finding the right place for both of us to continue treatment.

That day, for the first time I went by myself to the *gaushala*. As I fed the cows and got their blessings I saw a young guy around my age there with his father. He introduced himself as Uday. He then introduced me to his other friend Bunty who was also there with his father. They were both from Mumbai and had fathers with metastasized cancer. Instantly, I felt a connection. It was also a healthy change—rather than befriending the patients, I was getting close to the caregivers.

This was an important change. I remember my friend Adrienne in the US, emphasizing how important it was for me to not spend all my time around patients only. I had a tendency to get so involved with the disease and patients and doctors that I'd forget about life and things that I should enjoy and do at my age.

I suddenly had friends with whom I just chatted about movies, we would listen to songs, go for walks around the campus and the agenda was less cancer and more life. I was thankful for this development as it got me in the right mind-set to look beyond the hospital. As my health improved, I was beginning to feel there could be a chance that my life may perhaps go beyond the slated expiration date from the letter. While for anyone that would be an exciting prospect—for me it meant more challenges. I had been preparing to die for so long, I wasn't sure I knew how to plan to live. Time was a moving gift that I simply wanted should stand still.

CHAPTER 12

Singer For Sale

When love comes calling
Don't look back
When love comes calling
Don't look away
['Time After Time' by Cyndi Lauper]

'Are you a singer?' it started with a simple question. After over a month of a daily singing routine at the hospital, I was used to the compliments. But this question was slightly awkward. The man dressed in a crisp white shirt and white pleated slacks was asking me this as my body was covered in *gobar*.

While I normally did my morning and evening routine in the privacy of my room or at the odd-end hour, as my time there increased, I felt the need to continue this routine in the presence of the other patients. What prompted the change? I think perhaps my own confidence in not just sharing my cancer but also exposing my body for judgment. I was a grossly overweight man with body image issues coupled with cancer.

I think I was also willing to let others help me and spread the *gobar* on my tumours. When someone asks once, you think they are saying it for the sake of saying it, but when they ask repeatedly, you have to give them the benefit of doubt for sincerity. I let go of the judgment and let the other male caregivers help me. The two men who did this for me were young fathers, both with wives fighting uphill end stage cancer diagnoses.

I think the fact that they could actively do something for someone else (while they couldn't do it for their spouses, as the genders were separated for the *gobar* treatment areas) made them feel good. For me it was a strange experience. I didn't have an elder brother so my only male elder figure was my father. As they'd cover my stomach, my back and then my legs with *gobar*, I'd remember the times Dad would take out his medical kit when I'd cut myself or fall down. For these men—they may have thought of it as nothing, but for me—it was a gap that long needed to be filled.

As I answered the Man in White, I noticed he had been looking at my tumours. I simply responded to his initial question that I was not a professional singer but I loved to sing. He insisted that my voice was too good for the meeting hall at the hospital and I must, if not already, pursue singing as a career. While I knew my reality, the acknowledgement of this complete stranger to my childhood passion sparked something in me. He told me that his favourite song was '*Mere Desh Ki Dharti*' and that I should sing it that evening. I replied that I did not know the song well but would try. The Man in White inquired what was sermoned about me the previous night, at *bhajan* time.

After his hour-long nightly ritual, 'Hospital Dadaji' would like clockwork pass the microphone along to patients and attendants alike. As had become the routine, I'd be called up towards the end of that portion and I'd then sing whatever song I somewhat knew and that my Blackberry managed to secure the lyrics of from the internet. On the night in question, I had done an old Bollywood song '*Bhole O Bhole*' from the Amitabh Bachchan film 'Yaarana'. I had loved that song as a child and to be able to sing it and get the entire hospital team there to sing along with me, was such an inspiration.

But that particular night 'Hospital Dadaji' used his soapbox to drive a point home about the routine and the challenges of the treatment course. He singled me out as someone who had come from literally the other side of the world, to give this treatment a chance. What followed was almost a twenty-minute sermon about my story, my family (or lack thereof), my efforts and diligence at the hospital and finally how I was making the most of each and every day and embracing everything in a positive way.

While a good chunk of the audience understood 'Hospital Dadaji', the many non-Hindi speaking patients and attendants tried to decipher what exactly he was saying. In the crowd was an old woman in who I knew was Maharashtrian due to the way she wore her green sari. I had noticed her many times while singing. She and another Maharashtrian woman would almost constantly talk during *bhajan* time but when I'd sing, they'd actually close their eyes and listen.

Little did I know that that woman was the mother of the Man in White. He explained to me that she had battled cervical cancer undergoing treatment successfully near their Northern Karnataka hometown. After hearing me sing and walk around the campus alone, she wanted to speak with me but was unable to communicate because of language barriers. They assumed I had a support system in place because of my closeness with other patients and attendants. Only after hearing 'Hospital Dadaji's' speech and learning how grave my condition was did he reach out to me.

He asked me what my plans were after my stay at the hospital. I expressed to him my uncertainties in speaking definitively about my future. I was requesting the trustees to extend my time there again and perhaps maybe looking for a one bedroom flat in the Sevak area, where I'd be close enough to the hospital to still continue treatment and have access to the cow-related treatments that I wanted and needed to continue. He asked me if I believed that the treatment was working. I told him that honestly I wasn't sure but something was definitely happening. Whether it was a sense of belonging and purpose at the hospital or the actual physical transformation, I was realizing that, inspite of my illness, because of my increased energy levels, I was feeling better. I needed to continue the treatment but doing it alone was going to be challenging.

He interrupted me mid-thought and expressed his genuine sadness on hearing my struggles. He then shared his grief at the loss of his first wife, his son and other relatives in a fatal car crash many years ago. An emotional avalanche descended that no amount of time could disguise.

His openness about the accident and his loss was quite surprising. I have seldom seen grown Indian men share their feelings for those who have passed away and that too in a semi-public space. He wasn't just filling me in though, he was sharing the absence he felt without the woman he clearly still adored and the son who he imagined would be somewhere near my age.

Again I felt this connection that I had not felt in a long time. The 'fatherly' role that had been next to absent for the past eight years of my life, was stepping up in front of me without any solicitation from my end. He invited me to chat some more and come to his room and meet his mother after my *gobar* treatment.

As I went to my room to wash off the *gobar* I thought about my luck. There was something very strange happening.

I had read enough psychology books to know that I was transferring the emotional attachment. Yet I also knew, that like what Mom and I had experienced after her diagnosis and our journey alongside other patients while going through the treatment, I was building a community here. A community of people who cared for me, and not just in the moment, these strangers were becoming a new core component of my life and my time while in India.

That afternoon seemed to breeze by. I had developed a somewhat 'popular' status, like back in High School, I was greeted and welcomed by everyone and it seemed time would fly jumping from conversation to conversation. I noticed the Man in White gesturing to me after our afternoon *sabha*. It was clear that he wanted me to come over to his room and also meet his mother.

I walked my way towards him and we headed to his room. I saw his mother and another couple, the same woman who would sit with her during our evening *bhajan* time. Mohanlalji (as the Man in White finally introduced himself) had apparently conveyed my story to them (they all could only speak Marathi) and almost immediately, his mother started to tear up.

I could tell that she was genuinely concerned for me. She started to talk in Marathi and I tried to figure out what she was saying. Being somewhat fluent in Gujarati and Hindi, I was able to pick up a few of the words here and there, but otherwise I had no idea what she was saying. Mohanlalji tried to fill me in, but first let her speak until she finally stopped. He looked to me and said Mataji as he called her, was suggesting I come to Haasilgaon their village with them. They had experienced great loss in their life and she was unwilling to see me fight my battle alone.

117

I was deeply touched to see this woman, whom I couldn't even communicate with, offer me this. Mohanlalji went on to tell me that he had some acres of agricultural land in which he had several *desi* cows. I'd have no issue continuing my treatment, as he had built a small farm there in the middle of the land, where there was a room and I could stay as long as I needed, whether it be a day, a week, a month, a year or forever.

He then expressed his limitations as a local farmer, he said I'd be more than welcome as long as I was prepared for adjusting to the simple life there. He could guarantee me pure air, clean living and *desi* cows. But language would be an issue, as would the food given that my diet was very specific. Finally, he wasn't sure about the lifestyle and if I'd be able to manage without many things, that are considered a luxury, in rural India.

I told him that I'd not have a problem adjusting given that I was able to survive and thrive at the hospital. It was a truly genuine offer from their end. I graciously thanked them for the offer and told them I'd think about it. It was then that I realized that Mohanlalji's time at the hospital was actually coming to an end. They were slated to leave the next day. He shared all of his personal numbers with me and told me that as my time here would come to an end, he hoped I'd consider coming straight to Haasilgaon to be with them.

I left his room thinking about how and where life had taken me. Was I ready and or willing to go somewhere I didn't know; where I might not be able to communicate properly? This could be the place that would serve as a long-term solution to my continuing with the cow therapy.

I spoke to Uday and Bunty about my conversation. They seemed supportive but as urbanites and aware of my background, they suggested I look into options in Mumbai or even in Sevak.

I met with Umeshbhai who kindly invited me first to his home and then his office. Here he told me that I'd not be able to extend my time any further at the hospital, as there were limited beds and my extensions were now inhibiting new patients from coming and starting treatment. I understood this and he offered to help me find a place in Sevak where I would have continued access to the hospital and the cow therapy.

Over the next few days, I met with a broker to look at properties. I was somewhat optimistic about finding a place and just continuing my routine. At this point, I had the full support of the hospital staff and knowing that between Umeshbhai, Dr. Balsara, Fatima Didi and Romeshbhai all being there locally, perhaps it was meant to be. As I began to share my plans with them, Romeshbhai seemed concerned.

He urged me to make a trip to Bangalore first as he was planning to be there and meet his 'Guruji', Sri Sri Ravi Shankar. He proclaimed that my life would change for the better but I'd have to go to the ashram for this to happen. He suggested I contact them and share my story and in the interim he'd arrange for me to meet Sri Sri.

While I wasn't convinced that any one person had that ability, I also wasn't willing to question Romeshbhai's motives. He was going out of his way to be there for me. And given that he had Fatima Didi's complete trust that I thought so highly of, I took his offer quite seriously. After all, only after my visit to Shirdi did my life bring me back to the hospital. I can't say I was a believer of Sai Baba but that moment stuck with me—it was perhaps the catalyst that finally detached me from my relatives and put me on the road towards focusing solely on my health and my happiness.

As I went to look at flats in the Sevak area, I was daunted by the amount of effort and energy that would actually be required to set up a place. I had spent enough time in India to know that *'ho jayega'* was a much longer process in reality. With my focus being solely on my health, would I have the energy, the ability or even the will to set up a place of my own? I had left the US closing up all my affairs and was prepared to move into a nursing home, and now here I'm thinking of setting up a new home?

I contemplated on what to do, as the alarm clock was ticking now that I'd been given notice that I'd not be able to extend further at the hospital. As it happened, Mohanlalji had returned to Haasilgaon and he called me daily to check in and see how I was doing. He'd then echo his previous statements and ask me to come down and join them in Haasilgaon. I couldn't express how much those calls meant to me.

After weeks upon weeks of sitting around the hospital with a charged phone but no incoming calls, it was reassuring to actually have communication with someone concerned about how I was doing, rather than just what my plans were without offering any solutions. He told me that his roommates, from when we had the conversation, were planning to return to his area in three days and I should join them. As it happened, another father and son whom I had befriended were also from that region of Northern Karnataka. The son, Swaroop and I had become friendly. He was a lecturer and spoke English well, so we connected on a different level.

He actually managed to fill me in a little on Mohanlalji. While I didn't doubt his intentions, I was used to doing my homework before making any decision. I wanted to go with my gut but carrying little expectations at this point, any information would have been helpful. Swaroop assured me that Mohanlalji's concern and interest was genuine. 'Chairman' as he was known in many circles, had previously been involved in local and regional politics and was very well connected in the area. He may not have been a rich man but his heart was big and he had done quite a lot for the community and that if I went to stay with him and his family, I'd be in good hands.

As it turned out, they too were planning to leave in three days. They offered to accompany me if I wanted to leave with them and the other couple. As I began to think about things I wondered whether there was any harm in going to Mohanlalji's. Nobody since the Shahs had insisted so strongly for me to stay with them and not to worry.

I thought about things practically and began to put a plan together. I had wanted to go to Shimoga, which was also in Karnataka. Romeshbhai had invited me to Bangalore to meet Sri Sri. It seemed everything that I wanted to do was available to me in the South.

I knew there were about eleven days before Romeshbhai would be in Bangalore. If I left with Swaroop and company, I could spend a few days at Mohanlalji's, see how I liked it and if I could adjust, great, but if not, I could travel to Shimoga and then Bangalore. I also knew that my cousin Richa, the doctor who had offered her support was there. Given that I was also close to the three-month marker, I knew that my scan time was coming soon. I could meet her and get all my tests done and then depending upon the results, decide the next steps.

As I realized that this plan could actually work and made sense, I headed over to Swaroop and told him that I'd be ready to join them. I called up Mohanlalji who seemed ecstatic at my decision to come down to Haasilgaon. He then spoke with Swaroop and instructed him to make sure that I make it to Miraj Station properly without issue.

I informed 'Hospital Dadaji' and Umeshbhai of my plans and said if things didn't work out I'd return to the area and they seemed confident that I was in good hands. Umeshbhai reminded me of a simple truth. 'Those who want to help, help. You're going to be closer to nature, you will be okay'.

As I realized that my time at the hospital was coming to an end—it was bittersweet. How I had come to the hospital and how I was leaving was dramatically different. In the course of forty odd days, I had become a believer of so many things. I had let go of so much. While my future was still relatively uncertain both in the short-term and long-term there was one thing that was guiding me—my faith. The faith I had in myself, the people around me that were actually there and of course, the nature and the cows, I was living a life with less complications and more confidence. I knew the days ahead were going to be tough but just as Mohanlalji had rightfully stated, it was all about adjustment.

I had adjusted to my new realities in India and just like everything was a test, so too was my future. As long as I kept the right attitude, kept laughing and smiling there was not going to be an end date to my journey, until I was ready and willing.

I messaged my friends in the US to inform them of my next steps and I got unilateral support. They had been so instrumental in my life till that moment, yet I knew that perhaps my next step would isolate me even further than the hospital had already done. It didn't help that my phone was having problems and my internet was sparse. It seems fitting then that the day before I was to leave for Karnataka, my phone officially died. Whether I was willing to accept it or not—I was being forced to let go even further.

CHAPTER 13

The Friendly Farmer & The Foreigner

Let me turn all the tears
That you have cried into pearls
Hand them over to me
I'm gonna keep keep them for you
['Experience Pearls' by Ace of Base]

I was an avid 'The Amazing Race' fan. For years I'd been planning to do the trip with a friend, but I knew the physicality of the challenges would always be a hindrance. As someone with street smarts and a penchant for traveling, I knew I'd be a shoe-in for the adventure. Of course no level of preparedness had me ready for the trip to Haasilgaon.

Without internet, phone or contact with the outside world, I packed my belongings and prepared for the ride I was to take with the rest of the Karnataka gang to the train station. I said goodbye for the second time from the hospital. This time I didn't know where my life was going to take me.

I spoke to Mohanlalji and he seemed extremely excited about my arrival. He shared with me the good news that the extended family's only daughter was to be married within the week and that upon my arrival I would be attending the wedding. I wasn't sure exactly how to respond. I took a deep breath and thought that once I got there, I'd accordingly process and handle whatever came my way.

As the time approached and the rickshaw got there I realized from the get-go that my somewhat privileged way of traveling was no longer an option. Between the six of us and our entire luggage, it was a tight squeeze, I just put myself into the zone of accepting whatever may come and tried to remain positive about this next step.

When we reached the train station, we realized that we had gotten there far too early. On top of this, our train was going to be delayed. Every twenty—thirty minutes there was an announcement of further delays. We sat on the platform, letting hour after hour pass without any sign of the train. The evening train ended up reaching the platform at about 1:30 am. While the rest of the group boarded the 2nd class non-A/C sleeper compartment, I was traveling alone in the 2nd class A/C sleeper car. Thankfully they took ownership of my American suitcase and I simply boarded the train with my laptop bag.

The train was pitch black and I slowly tried to find my berth but it was so dark I couldn't even find the numbers. When I did, I noticed that two men were sleeping on my berth. I tried to find a rail employee only to realize that everyone was sleeping. After almost ten minutes of tapping and attempting to wake a railway employee, he and I got to my seat and the men sleeping there went to their respective berths. The railway attendant looked at me and asked me if I was a patient.

I wasn't sure if he knew because of my ticket or it had been flagged or because of how I looked after the eight plus hours of commuting and waiting from the hospital to the station platform. I said I needed rest and to please tell me when we reach Miraj Junction (the station where I was to depart).

I was getting stressed as Miraj approached, I had no idea how long the train would stop there and without an operating phone or any idea of where I was, what would happen if I missed my stop. The anxiety had me making multiple rounds to the restroom. Each time I'd get up, I would try to find a different railway employee hoping they'd give me the same answer as the last time but instead, I'd be told something else. Unable to calculate because of the delays plus the unusual stop-and-go behaviour of the train, it was maddening not to know exactly when I'd reach.

Thankfully a young English speaking man was packing up to de-board and he told me that my stop would be just one station after his, and it wouldn't be more than half an hour's time away. I was grateful and began to get ready. As I was doing this, I saw a familiar face. Swaroop had come to check up on me and inform me that I'd need to get down on the next station. I was thankful to him and soon enough we had reached Miraj Station.

Swaroop and his dad stayed with me as they had promised Mohanlalji. Parched and thirsty they wished to eat something. I was sceptical of having anything, unaware of how long my day would be and where I'd end up and what my access to toilets would be like, so I opted against it. I waited where Mohanlalji had told me to stand, after informing him I had reached. Within forty five minutes or so, he pulled up in a Mahindra Bolero and thanked Swaroop and his dad for escorting me into his custody.

With Mohanlalji was another man, introduced to me as his friend and relation, Manavji. It was clear they were very close, but what was interesting was that there was a dynamic at play. Friendship or relationship aside Manavji was clearly his 'go to' guy. The stories Swaroop and others had shared with me about Mohanlalji started to come alive for me, very vividly.

As we left Miraj Station, I was informed that there would be a few stops along the way as a result of the upcoming wedding. They told me I'd be okay. It wasn't a question but rather how things were going to be. We stopped for a quick bite at a 'safe' restaurant, I was consuming food with normal taste and no medicine snuck in it, after almost thirty days.

The day continued with multiple stops through several small towns and villages. It was a perfect prelude to the life and lifestyle I was soon to become accustomed to, now that I was here. As I was introduced in Hindi to the many people I met, the dialogue seemed to end there, as everything else was spoken in either Marathi or Kannad. I could somewhat understand some phrases and words in Marathi but Kannad had no similarities to any language I spoke. I truly felt like the friendly sick alien had arrived in town.

As the sun began to set, we finally made our way to Haasilgaon. We first stopped at Manavji's home, which was just outside the village. The house seemed decent enough, very clean and organized. I soon realized that Manavji's background was from the army and it suddenly all made sense. I assumed Mohanlalji's farm would be similar but I still had time before getting there. I took a bath at their insistence before we headed for dinner in the village. Pulling out a fresh pair of clothes from my oversized suitcase, I headed to the tiny bathroom, a shed to the side of the home. I had a typical bucket bath yet again, something I had gotten used to as a result of my hospital life.

The toilet was next to the 'bath' room. In all my time in India thus far I had been lucky to find only western toilets.

My good fortune ended that evening as I encountered my first squat toilet. I wasn't a stranger to the toilet but I hadn't needed to squat in many years. Given my size, my physical challenges and quite the bad back, I was concerned. I knew I didn't have a choice so I tried my best to adjust to my new reality. It pained a little, was mildly uncomfortable but I somehow managed my first use. I secretly prayed that Mohanlalji's farm would have a western toilet, I'd soon find out that was not going to be the case anywhere in Haasilgaon.

We made our way into the village and I swear I felt I had landed on a Bollywood soundstage. Every image I had of the typical village and the running kids, the random bull or cow, the staring old women sitting outside their homes on cots; every cliché was becoming my reality. We finally reached Mohanlalji's home and it was filled with people. I didn't understand if they were there to greet me, or there for the upcoming wedding or just there because that's the norm.

I immediately walked over to Mataji (whose name I was yet to learn). She embraced me and looked so happy to see me in her home. She then stepped back into another room and I realized that the men would be sitting in one room and the women were all in the other (which it turns out was the kitchen). I shook hands and spoke to countless men who tried to engage me in conversation with their limited Hindi and spotty English.

There was a lot of warmth in that room but also a lot of curiosity. I think we all wondered if I'd be able to adjust. The room was set up very like the *sabha* hall. Everyone was seated on the floor (as there was no furniture in the room other than one bed and a Godrej cabinet). I sat on an all-too-familiar plastic chair that had greeted me daily at the hospital. I could smell garlic and onions being cooked and soon the chai and snacks were distributed. I was clearly well past my hospital eating schedule but Mataji was aware of this and informed me dinner would soon be ready.

There was no table so I suggested that I'd join everyone else and sit down on the floor and try to eat. They were hesitant but allowed me as I wished. As we all sat down to eat, I noticed that the women in the kitchen were not even allowed to attend to us. They passed along the dishes to the younger boys of the house who served us on our platters. Mohanlalji informed me that everything was vegetarian and Mataji had ensured nothing was too spicy. She knew of my diet at the hospital and had tried to accommodate me as best as possible. I was so drawn by the garlic and onion smell that I knew I was going to have no qualms in breaking the Jain rules. My family was Jain but the idea of no onion and garlic in our food was just out of the question for me. Especially after my conversation with Dr. Balsara in Sevak, I also knew about the medical benefits of both ingredients, so I was going to make up for the forty plus days without the taste of either!

The dinner was truly amazing; *jowar ki roti, methi ki subzi, dordka ki subzi and moong dal varan.* I wasn't sure if similar to my snack earlier in the day, it was the fact that the tastes were not similar to any of my hospital meals or if the food was actually good, but that dinner ranked as one of the best ones I'd ever had in my life. Mataji seemed genuinely pleased to see me eating and enjoying my dinner. It's strange how food can be such a comfort and how love can be so easily felt through cooking. Everything in the hospital's kitchen was done with the same intent, but so many failed to see that.

Clearly seeing the exhaustion in my eyes after a long trip, Mohanlalji suggested heading to the farm and getting me settled there. As we made our way, I saw how empty and isolated the road was as soon as we left the village. I noticed that we passed Manavji's home to the right. No other home or light came from either side. Mohanlalji mentioned that at night the area got many foxes and snakes so to be careful. It was a short car drive, we were about 5 kms from the Haasilgaon village.

As we entered his property, a grand rough road greeted us. I wasn't sure what I had signed up for but I saw on both sides acres upon acres of grapes followed by sugarcane.

The farm looked similar to Manavji's with the exception of two things. One—a giant water reserve just steps away from the 'home' and two—this was not a 'home' but truly a 'farm'. There were several doors from outside. One opened into a small office with desk and chair followed by a plexiwall with a door to enter a room with a bed. That was to be my bedroom. As we walked out, he showed me the farm's great room with a television and platform mattresses for guest. The next room was the farm's warehouse where all the fertilizers, pesticides, seeds and everything else were stored. From there, he walked me to an adjacent building where there was a small kitchen that was presently housing a family of four who were the caretakers of the property. In the back, another family stayed, they too looked out for the farm and all of Mohanlalji's matters. As we walked across the large rocks, there was another shed. One room housed the squat toilet I had been praying against (which also in turn had no water or light). The adjacent room was for taking a bath (there were two huge open windows with no glass and no kind of plumbing).

As we walked further, I realized we had made a circle and I saw ultimately what I was there for—his *gaushala*. In it housed several beautiful *desi* cows. As it was night time most of them were resting. The farm hand Ajay and his two young sons introduced me to my new friends— Sakhshi, Gauri, Ganga... I honestly couldn't remember the rest of their names as it went on. My eyes were immediately drawn to Sakhshi. She wasn't the typical *desi* cow. She was black & white like a Jersey cow. Her hair was softer and silkier than any other cow I'd ever seen. She was gentle and it felt like she was looking right at me. As I moved around the *gaushala*, her eyes followed me. It's a strange thing to have an instant connection with an animal, especially for me, but after almost two months of relatively anonymous cow time, to see first-hand the cows, that were going to be there for me, it was both humbling and slightly intimidating. It's probably the first time I felt like a cow was judging me and not the other way around.

We finished the circle and made our way around the water reserve back to the main entrance. Mohanlalji had his twenty-something son Devjeet, home on break from his college and there to attend his cousin sister's wedding, take my suitcase and put it in the bedroom. He asked if I'd need anything at night, I said I should be fine. He got me a flashlight in case I needed to use the bathroom. He suggested I simply walk to the rocks on the side if I needed to pee and use the toilet if otherwise. He instructed Ajay to put a small bucket of water in the bathroom in case I needed. As I tried to open my bag, I saw Mohanlalji and his son both begin to disrobe in front of me. It wasn't unusual as I thought they were going to change for the night until I realized that their night suit was simply their undershirt and underwear. As I took out my long shirt and long pajamas, they wished me good night and headed to the great room.

I very selfishly didn't ask either of them if they preferred to sleep on the bed, as it was a queen-sized bed. As they left, I was instructed to make sure to lock the door from inside, as an open door could be an invitation to an unwanted creature of any kind. As they headed to the great room with a couple of other friends of Mohanlalji, also disrobed, I realized that I had forgotten my manners and asked Devjeet if anyone wanted to bunk in the bedroom. He politely said that room was just for me 'sir'. I asked him not to call me that but he seemed shy and a bit overexcited by my presence there. I was reminded of the fact as to how ironic it was that I was now there with these men. Mohanlalji himself had suffered a great loss and just as I felt him stepping into a fatherly role for me at the hospital, my entrance into Haasilgaon felt like the return of a grandson, son and now older brother.

As I saw the four men sleeping side by side on the mattresses, I thought about how lucky I was and what selfless heights other individuals will go to accommodate someone. It reminded me of my childhood days and how when we'd visit India, all my cousins and I would sleep like that and watch television till late at night or listen to music or tell jokes. These days, there was no room for me despite countless empty bedrooms.

It's very sentimental to wish for what we had, but it comes at a price. All the luxuries in the world couldn't replace the love, the warmth, the feeling of worth those few hours had already given me in Haasilgaon. What I had so longed for—the memories that comforted me of India from my past—were happening again. It wasn't the family I expected to have but it was a family, and they were accepting, willing to care for me and make me feel at home.

As I went to my room and locked the door behind me, I thought about the last twenty four hours and how my life had taken me to yet another strange place that yet again felt instantly like home. I didn't know what was going to be in store for me when I woke up, but that night my first night living on the farm, a few kilometres away from the village, a few hundred kilometres away from anyone that knew me—I was going to be okay.

I did my *Navkar Mantra* and then one '*Om ka jaap*' before going to sleep. As I closed my eyes, the electricity went out. The room had no circulation, as there were no windows. The inverter played the fan with a rather loud buzzing sound. I was now used to the heat and the sweat. It was actually milder than in Sevak so I turned off the fan and simply fell asleep. The silence was only interrupted by my breath, which got lighter and lighter as the still night turned in to a new day.

CHAPTER 14

The Village Voice

It's not about the money money money
We don't need your money money money
We just want to make the world dance
Forget about the price tag
['Price Tag' by Jessie J]

On my first morning in the village, everything felt staged. From the early morning roosters to the farm hands bathing naked outside to me struggling to make my way to the bathroom with a roll of toilet paper, I was experiencing the typical city to village transitional culture shock.

As prepared as I thought I was after my time at the hospital, the village and in particular the farm life was not something I was used to. My idea of camping was limited to private clubs and organized trips that included the rustic option of sleeping in pre-set luxury tents. Yet, despite the dramatic change from my luxury doorman living in New York to now a borderline rustic farm, I managed to find my way very quickly. As it turned out, the farm was still under construction. Mohanlalji had not shared this news with me prior to my arrival, so I'd have to be taken to Manavji's place for a bath as there was no hot water and the bathroom was not complete.

Still dressed in my pajamas, I saw Devjeet jump into the reservoir leaving his towel and soap on the side. The water was far from clean, as the monsoon coupled with the dirt around the premises had made it quite muddy. Still, that seemed to be the place to simply jump in and take a bath, not to mention, have a swim. The reservoir was over fifty feet. I had not swum in several years and given the condition of the water (not to mention the temperature of the water) this was something I was not going to partake on my first day.

As I saw Mohanlalji join him, I walked over towards the *gaushala* and saw the cows for the first time in daylight. I introduced myself to Sakhsi, Gauri, Ganga and the rest of the crew. I noticed there were also two Jersey cows and one bull. The cows were dramatically different from the Gir cows I had gotten to know and trust at Laxmiprasad. As I spoke to the main caretaker Ajay, about the cows, he mentioned the different breeds. I was drawn by their long horns that were painted bright orange.

I asked as to why that was done. It was done on the *Mattu Pongal* day, a day that celebrated prosperity of the land and the *desi* cows were considered a holy blessing for the land. In all my time at the hospital, for all the prayers and blessings we were taking and giving the cows—this intimacy between man and cow felt far more intense. There was a loving relationship between two specific animals. It was one of appreciation and reverence. I tried to pet one of the *desi* cows but Ajay stopped me before I could. He informed me that they weren't the friendliest and will not hesitate to kick me straight out of the *gaushala*.

I was somewhat taken back since I had had such a peaceful experience with the cows in Sevak. In fact none of the cows at the hospital *gaushala* were tied up, while here all of them were tied up. I understood why they might not be as friendly. Just as I stepped away, I saw Ganga start to urinate. Ajay already knew about my condition and he had a stainless steel container ready, he ran to grab it and place it to catch Ganga's *gaumutra.*

I watched in amazement. She was literally giving me morning medicine. Despite the many hours I had spent at the *gaushala,* I was not privy to seeing the cows give milk or the labourers gather the *gaumutra* and *gobar.* But standing here in the *gaushala,* I knew that no matter what lay ahead—being here was a good thing—not just for my health but my soul.

As the container was overflowing, Ajay handed it to me. I thanked him and he told me that normally the first *gaumutra* of the cow is the most potent and starting tomorrow he'd make arrangements to get it earlier. I told him that I'd like to do it myself. He questioned whether I'd be able to get up so early. I told him that I was used to be being up by 5:00 am or sometimes even earlier so it would not be problem. He seemed somewhat surprised, then assured me that I'd not need to be there that early but by 6:30-7:00 am would be the best time.

He then walked over to the reservoir to fill a pail with water. It apparently was his prep time before milking the cows. I saw from afar that his mother, Ajji was making her way to the *gaushala* to help him.

She started to speak to me in Marathi, but to no avail. It was clear that this woman had spent her life around these animals. Her comfort in moving them around and bossing them into getting into their respective places as required, was clearly a routine. As she sat herself down below Ganga, I knew it was milk time.

Ajay had cleaned Ganga up nicely in order to get Ajji ready to milk her. Ganga was pregnant. It was clear she was not very compliant in giving milk at the time but Ajji's insistence meant she was not going to take no for an answer.

Hesitantly Ganga started to give milk and I watched in marvel. After her *gaumutra*, she was now blessing me with her milk. Ajji mentioned to me that if I wanted, I could have the raw milk. I was unsure but had spoken to Dr. Balsara about it. While there was fear of bacteria as the cow was being milked, if consumed immediately the risks are minimal. I was surprised as to how warm it was as she handed over the milk to me. While I wasn't likely to have the milk then and there on my first day, it was something I was going to look into later.

By then Mohanlalji had made his way over to the *gaushala*. He could see my fascination with the cows. He went on to explain a little further about the history of the specific cows. He introduced me to Radha, a rather old looking cow on the other end of the *gaushala*. She had apparently been the *desi* cow of his family, all of his and his brother's children grew up on her milk. She was now quite old and fading away but he knew it was the right thing for her to stay with them till the end, no matter what. He may have been speaking about the cow but it was clear he was also reassuring me, as this was a much more foreign world than even the hospital.

As I was holding the milk, he too suggested I consume it raw, but I had not yet had my morning *gaumutra* so I told him that I could do that the next day. Given that I did not drink tea or coffee, he suggested that I take warm fresh milk in the morning. I agreed.

He then walked me around a little through the farm. To one side there were acres upon acres of banana trees. It was the first time in India that I'd been around so much agriculture. To the other side there were endless small trees. I didn't actually recognize them from afar but upon closer look I realized that they were pomegranate trees.

It was the first season and while not traditional for the local environment, Mohanlalji was taking a risk to try and grow the tricky fruit on his land. We walked a little further to reach what was a familiar site, the track our car had taken to bring me there the night before. It was covered by sugarcane on either side and further ahead, acres and acres of grapes, that too in its first season.

As he shared, much of the farm was relatively newly acquired land and other areas near the village had the majority of his and his family's sugarcane and grapes. This land was his attempt to move from a small time farmer to a bigger regional agriculturalist. While he kept sharing, my focus was centred on the numerous wild trees growing around the property. I saw countless trees of *neem*, gynema and curry leaves. Ecstatic at being able to correctly identify the trees, I started to take some leaves of each tree. Mohanlalji seemed surprised but I told him that this was something I had started at the hospital. During one of my conversations with Dr. Balsara, I had questioned him about the *tulsi* water we as patients were supposed to drink throughout the day. I was a fan of *tulsi* and was wondering if it would have the same effect if I simply consumed the leaves directly from the tree. He believed there to be little difference. From that day onwards, I had made it a point to head to the *tulsi* tree and grab fresh leaves. Ditto for gynema, neem and curry leaves.

As Mohanlalji noticed me, I realized I looked like an excited kid in an Ayurveda candy shop. He then showed me fresh Gingerroot and turmeric at the other side of his farm. I was thrilled as I discovered one thing after another. I told him that as long as I was to stay there, I'd like to eat as raw and natural as possible from the land. He heartily agreed and pleaded with me to speak to his Mataji who had apparently stopped some of the treatment from the hospital already. He was hoping that I'd be able to convince her to stick along with the course and perhaps with my presence, she'd feel like she wasn't doing it alone. Of course I agreed.

Mohanlalji's family lived between the village and by their main grape farm. My room was in the godown several kilometres away. As a result, he believed I'd not come in between his family or his family's life and I could feel at home. He showed me at the back where additional rooms were going to be built for the labour and soon enough the kitchen would be empty and then I'd also be able to cook for myself (he knew that I enjoyed to prepare my meals by myself).

But for now, I had to get ready for my trip to Manavji to take a bath. Upon finishing the *gaumutra* and milk with some warm *upma* that Ajji had made, I instantly felt uneasy. It was clear that Ganga's liquids were making their way through my system too quickly. I rushed to the bathroom, which thankfully I reached in time.

It was clear that the new atmosphere, the new cows (for me) and this new life were going to take some time to settle in. After feeling relieved, I headed back and a bike was waiting to take me to Manavji.

With my back already an issue, getting around from point A to point B (namely from the farm to the village) was not going to be easy. The majority of the farmers had motorbikes, as this was their main mode of transportation. For my body and in particular my spine, this was something I wasn't sure I could handle. Still without any other options, it was my only way to get to civilization so I needed to adjust to this reality.

Its strange how certain items we wouldn't necessarily consider luxury, truly are. Hand in hand with motorcycles was the sitting issue. I was not accustomed to having to sit on the floor, let alone eating on the floor. I quickly discovered that each house had at least one chair, that same ubiquitous plastic chair that had become my best friend at the hospital. I couldn't proclaim that it was comfortable but at least it alleviated some of my pain.

As I reached Manavji's home, I was introduced to a young woman who I discovered was Manavji's wife. Similar to my experience the night before in the village at Mohanlalji's home, I noticed a trend, the wives were significantly younger than their husband. It wasn't weird other than the fact that they all had children relatively closer to my age which meant that they had gotten married as young teenagers. Shobha *Bhabhi*, Manavji's wife, had heated my water and walked from the home to the bathroom with a warm water bucket. She then offered me a second breakfast, which I declined but got somewhat pushed into having a little bit.

As I went to take my second bath in the village, Manavji told me that there was soap inside for washing clothes so I could wash my underwear there and leave it for drying. I wasn't quite sure what to do, as I hadn't even thought about my laundry. At the hospital, I had thankfully got one of the women sweeping the rooms to wash my clothes. It was normally not allowed and it was the job of the caregiver to handle this but I did not have a caregiver. For the few days that Madhvi aunty was there, she kindly offered to do my laundry but for the rest of the time, I got permission from Umeshbhai to get one of the staff members to do it for me.

As I began to see and understand rural life, I realized that not only were there no washing machines, there was also no one I could pay to do these chores. I simply nodded to

Manavji and said I'd do it at the farm, not sure exactly what to say. I was grateful for one upgrade from the hospital, hot water. It had been a long time since I had seen as much hot water as I had in that pail. While I had caregivers get me water at the hospital, by the time the water would make its way to bath time, it would become rather lukewarm and given that our showers were early in the morning, it wasn't necessarily soothing.

Given my back pain, the hot water immediately brought relief. As I washed up and got ready I realized that I too would need to be like the local men and come out in a towel and then put my clothes on. It may sound like a trivial thing, but for me, getting dressed or undressed publicly was such an uncommon occurrence and that too in front of strangers (the farm labourers who had arrived to cut sugarcane). But they didn't care, I was the only one with the complex. I had no choice but to get over it. As I got dressed I noticed that Mohanlalji had made his way to me.

He was kindly checking in on me. As I was ready, he suggested we go to the grape farm and meet Mataji and Abbaji (his father), the only person from his immediate family that I had not met the night before. As we took his bike, we approached what I could only explain as a traditional *jhuggi*. I thought the labour was staying there only to realize that was Mataji and Abbaji's room. It was such a stark contrast to how I had been introduced to the rest of Mohanlalji's world, I was confused but left my questions to the side as I sat with Mataji and asked her about her health.

She shared with me her disgust for the Laxmiprasad treatment. She had managed to keep taking the medicines but did not enjoy the *desi* cow components or the meals. I was surprised that she had so quickly given up but she refused to budge and felt that whatever will happen she's fine with it. It was amusing then for her to be making sure that I follow the treatment to the T. She informed Mohanlalji that she had already debriefed the women in the village about my food restrictions but I'd need to give them further details to ensure that there'd be no issues with my meals.

Mohanlalji suggested that I have lunch and dinner in the village at his home, until the family living in the kitchen moved to the backside and the kitchen would be open at the farm. Before I had even said anything about my clothes, he also said that I should leave my dirty clothes in the village and his wife would wash them for me. I was a little hesitant but I knew I didn't have a choice. However if history was any indication, I knew that my days here were going to be numbered. While Mataji had invited me and Mohanlalji had arranged and encouraged me to come without issue, I knew that my arrival was going to add work for people who had not consented to my being there. I had just spent time, before the hospital, with countless relatives where I knew even having a meal with them had become a large chore/challenge. I wasn't willing to impose that on others.

At that moment, I was confident that I'd spend a few days with Mohanlalji and then proceed with my plans of Shimoga and Bangalore. I didn't tell Mohanlalji of this but mentally my mind was now not going to get too comfortable.

As Mataji and I sat and attempted our song-dance of a conversation between her Marathi and my Hindi, Devjeet came by and asked me if I wanted to come into the village as Mohanlalji was being called for some event. I agreed and made my way for the first time in broad sunlight into the village.

The first thing I noticed as we made our way into the village was how much agriculture landscaped the neighbouring areas. To either side of the rather well paved road into the village I saw countless bowel deposits. I was a little surprised to notice this. It was a sight I was used to seeing when seated on a local Mumbai train looking out, but outside this beautiful little village surrounding by so many crops—I didn't understand this.

As we made it to the first T in the village, Devjeet began to show me the landmarks, the local bank, the local *panwala*, he then took me down a narrow short cut path. We stopped in front of Dhanushji's home. Unlike the other village homes, his looked 'western'. He introduced himself and his wife, Rakhee Didi, who I assumed could possibly not be older than I was and then I met their two children, Shruti and Amrut. Dhanushji like Manavji was a former Army man, who had retired after several years of service, to return back to their home village and now spent his time as a farmer.

As I spoke to them, Amrut kept distracting my concentration. He couldn't be more than nine or ten years old. His face was so inquisitive and it was clear that I was fascinating him. Whether it was my size, my colour (I was much lighter in skin that most of the villagers), my accent or the fact that I was from America, he was hooked. Rakhee Didi also seemed a little unlike the other women I had met the night before. She was a little bold and actually spoke directly to me, even while in front of her husband. She mentioned that Amrut had been asking them so many questions since they heard I had come. I then

143

started to try and converse with Amrut but he suddenly got very shy.

Devjeet tried to get Amrut more comfortable but he was going to take time to warm up. Devjeet suggested we go upstairs. I wasn't quite sure why but it appeared that Manavji's brother, Sharadji another former Army man, whose son had returned from Bangalore and gotten married, was now trying to set up a BPO in the village, a first for the community.

His temporary setup was in Dhanushji's enclosed roof. As I went upstairs, I met Sanjay (Sharadji's son) and after so many days of disconnection, thanks to my broken phone, I was going to have access to the internet and the rest of the world. Devjeet suggested I stay there till lunch and then I could head to his house. Sanjay agreed to show me the way to their home.

Sanjay had spent a few years in Bangalore and was able to speak decent English (according to Devjeet he was the best English speaker in the village). It was nice to actually have a conversation, which was not in broken Hindi after the past couple of days, so I knew that his office was going to become my refuge while staying there.

As I opened up my email for the first time in many days, I felt such a disconnection. I knew I needed to inform friends back in the US that I had arrived safely and that things were okay but somehow it seemed almost like what I was doing and where I had ended up was too hard to believe. Two hours flew by in a moment's notice as I wrote message after message. I tried to explain my new reality and what I was doing to all those souls that had been there for me through some of the most challenging moments of my life.

I needed to feel that I had their support through this chapter of my life but I wasn't quite sure I was going to be able to communicate too often.

Amrut ran upstairs with two other boys, Amoljeet (Mohanlalji's son) and Pranak (Mohanlalji's brother Mahadev's son). They had come to receive me and take me to their home for lunch. They seemed mesmerized by my laptop. It was my one prize possession that had made the journey with me. It had special significance as I had bought it literally the day before I started chemotherapy for the first time. My 17" Macbook Pro had stayed with me while so many others had left me behind. But even its age was starting to alarm me. I was no longer able to use her with the battery in. Within a couple of minutes, the laptop would crash. As a result, since before coming to India, I kept the laptop plugged in and simply kept the battery out to avoid any crashes. Of course in the US I didn't have electricity randomly going out. My first lesson was at the hospital where the electricity came and went throughout the day and night.

Mohanlalji had already warned me about the electricity issues. While he had an inverter for the farm, it was an issue. There were times that there'd be no electricity for twelve-eighteen hours straight. I was not looking forward to finding this out.

As I approached Mohanlalji's house for the first time, I went past the living room and entered the kitchen. Mohanlalji had two brothers and their respective wives plus Mohanlalji's own wife who were formally introduced to me. Two of them were preparing my lunch while I saw one was taking care of the buffalos and cows that they housed behind their home. Devjeet informed me that they raised the animals for milk. I noticed a literal swamp of *gobar* to the

145

side. He explained to me that they put all the *gobar* there as they ran gas in their home through the *gobar*. It was the first time I had ever heard of *gobar* gas but at this point in my journey, I was not surprised to hear anything when it came to the power and ability of cows. To see first-hand the *gobar* converted into gas for the cooking of my meal, I was further made dependent on these holy animals it seemed.

The Bhabhi's as I called them seemed quite reserved at first but as they saw that I was playing with Amoljeet and Pranak, inquiring about their school and asking questions, their suspicion of me subsided. I then met the daughter of the house, Reema. She was to be married in two days and the house seemed to be busy preparing for the big day. Devjeet seemed to have been given the responsibility to make sure that I was okay. As the two of us sat to have lunch, the plastic chair was brought into the kitchen area. As there was no table, the youngest Bhabhi Pranak's mom, Geeta Bhabhi (she lived with Mataji at the grape farm) suggested taking two of the big storage containers and putting one of the table trays atop for my *thali*.

The food of course smelled great. They had tried to follow the instructions that Mataji had suggested. There was *moong dal, lasooni methi* vegetable and they were making a fresh *jowar ki roti* for me. I was thrilled as it reminded me of the *dhaba* lunch I had had with my cousin Kushal on the way back from Shirdi. Reema's mom, Kavita Bhabhi seemed to be the most inquisitive about me. As I was eating, she began to ask about my time in America but more importantly about my family.

Devjeet seemed to have some power as he veered the conversation away from the touchy subject and told Amoljeet to turn on the television. For the first time since before going to the hospital I was seeing a television.

Of course, it may as well have been switched off as the channels were mainly in Marathi. To appease me Devjeet turned on a Bollywood film channel. He asked if that was okay, I said I wasn't too interested. Pranak and Amoljeet jumped on my indifferent response and immediately switched the television to cartoons.

It was a strange thing, I noticed. Despite a different culture, new people, a foreign language and a completely different environment from anything I had ever experienced, I was quickly made to feel at home. At this point, I was realizing that no matter where I went—I was going to make it my home.

CHAPTER 15

AV America

Like a lightning bolt to the heart
You woke me up woke me up
Yeah you brought me out of the dark
With just one spark just one spark
Now I can feel your pulse
Kick starting this lifeless soul
Like a lightning bolt to heart
You woke me up woke me up
['Lightning' by Cash Cash]

Amoljeet and Pranak were eagerly waiting for me to finish my lunch. It was clear they wanted more time with me. Devjeet asked if I wanted to rest. I wasn't particularly tired so he suggested that I could go back to Sanjay's office. I agreed and immediately Amoljeet and Pranak offered to walk me over there. As I walked the village roads, I noticed the stares. I wasn't just a normal guest. They were taking pride in their 'American' guest. I could see Amrut and his cousin Aayan run towards me at about the halfway point between both houses. As we all walked together, Amrut asked me how far America was. As I began to answer his questions, I realized that I was building my very own village fan club. It reminded me of my childhood trips to India when my younger cousins would huddle around me and ask about my life in the US.

But these days with most of them well travelled and exposed to everything Western, the curiosity was gone. To see the genuine interest from these boys—it felt good. After all, we all wanted to feel needed besides feeling loved. Their questions offered me a chance to share a part of myself that was quickly becoming a distant memory, because of the countless experiences that I was having since coming to India.

As we reached Amrut's home, his mom suggested that while I was in the village, I should sit with the boys and teach them about the world, help them with their English and get them all straightened out rather than them just wandering around and wasting time watching bad television. I was already thinking the same thing but it was reaffirming to have someone want that.

I formally introduced myself to Aayan, who seemed to be the most at-ease kid I'd met so far in the village. He referred to me, as 'Americawala bhaiya' which I thought was quite the appropriate name for me. After all, no matter how local I was to become, I'd always be the foreigner to them. America was nothing more than a dream for the locals, their image of where I had come from was a combination of Bollywood scenery and knowledge from their class about President Obama.

It was refreshing to have my identity diversify from being the cancer patient to something past that. It was an unexpected twist of my time in Haasilgaon that felt like a blessing in a different kind of way. Sanjay asked me to join him upstairs but I felt more at home playing with the boys and answering their endless supply of questions. While I found their curiosity endearing, the adults of the village found it to be a nuisance. Maybe it was that they didn't have the answers or they felt learning was a waste of time, but for me, it took me back to my academic world. While I wasn't used to teaching elementary school students, it was lovely to be able to share knowledge. That the knowledge was not cancer related—that was the real bonus.

The afternoon went by so quickly, I didn't realize that the sun was coming down. Devjeet came by to check in on me. He was surprised that I had not even made my way upstairs to Sanjay's office, I was so busy with the boys. Rakhee Didi offered me a mid-afternoon snack and suggested I eat dinner there. I asked Devjeet if that was okay to which he said you could decide that 'sir'. Mohanlalji had clearly told me that no house was off limits for me. He seemed to have such a warm relationship with so many of the families and given that they were in some ways related, they were are all one big family.

For me, I was exploring the range of relationships. Rakhee Didi seemed genuinely concerned and as a result it felt easy to be myself around her and her family. As I accepted and thanked her for the invitation to stay for dinner, she very nonchalantly stated that even though their pockets may be limited, their hearts were wide open. She then went on to say that I was welcome to join them at any time for any meal. Again, it was such a dramatic change from what I had become accustomed to hearing since coming to India.

I sat for dinner on what was quickly becoming my infamous plastic chair and had another tasty meal. It was hotter than I could handle but luckily there was yogurt to counter the spices. As had been my habit, I shared with Rakhee Didi some ideas for recipes. She was surprised that I knew so much about cooking. It seemed I had not only piqued her interest but Amrut and Shruti who had joined me for dinner were requesting I make some dishes.

I said after Reema's wedding, I'd be sure to make a dish or two for everyone. They were genuinely excited. As I finished dinner, Mohanlalji came by to see how I was doing. As we all sat down, he filled us in on all the running around he had done throughout the day for the wedding. He told me that they were going to have a simple wedding as his circle was too large and if he invited everyone he knew, there would be thousands. I wasn't sure if he was bragging or stating a fact but I knew time would tell.

And it certainly did. I was quite surprised by how truly simple the wedding was. Although apparently, this was much fancier than the usual for the area. To one side of the wedding hall, I saw what looked like a full-home gift hamper. In reality, it was a display of what Reema's family was giving her to take with her—her dowry of sorts. It was interesting to see that while the bride and groom were making their way to the stage, people were mentally jotting down the furniture, kitchen appliances and showpieces that would make their way to her new home. What surprised me even more was the dress code. Most of the men came in normal pant and shirts. The women dressed a little more formally but it was a stark contrast to what I could now describe as the glitzy and glamorous Gujarati and Punjabi weddings I was used to attending.

The wedding proved a coming-out party of sorts for me. All the locals who had heard about Mohanlalji's new friend came to meet and greet me. On one side there was the wedding and on the other, here I was, equally exposed and making my official debut with the who's who of the community.

While Mohanlalji had mentioned that the wedding was going to be a quiet affair, I quickly realized he meant what he said, that this was just the tip of the iceberg in terms of his contacts and relations. I also realized that the devotion that Manavji had shown for Mohanlalji was nothing compared to so many who came and attended the wedding and bowed down to Mohanlalji. To me he may have been a stranger offering a helping hand, but this was not something new for him. It was clearly evident that he had positively affected a lot of people's lives and they revered him. I was feeling incredibly lucky and the doubts that I had started having about staying there were again questioned. Perhaps I'd be able to stay in Haasilgaon longer than I was planning.

By the evening, calmness once again prevailed over the village, after the morning excitement of the wedding. As I walked on my way, after taking a little rest at Amrut's house over to Mohanlalji's place, each house was now feeling familiar. The faces that had seemed to blend into one another were now distinct. I was learning names and families. Seeing the kindness and well wishes that were being sent my way I felt even stronger than at the hospital. Haasilgaon may have had about 2000 villagers but the power of all of them knowing my story and wanting to be there for me in whatever way was truly touching. As I walked around, I got stopped and invited in for *chai* and *poha*. I now understood that if I needed to pass the time, I could simply wander from home to home if I chose to.

Of course, I wanted to be productive and if I was going to spend time with people, I wanted to make sure I was able to give something back. It seemed, similar to the hospital, my ability to share knowledge, albeit less about cancer and more about general knowledge was going to be my main contribution.

In a matter of three days, I realized in what way I was going to connect with different groups within the village.

With the kids, it was going to be geography, English and general knowledge. With the ladies, food and sharing recipes. With the gents, farming, agriculture and business. Of course my past, my history and my thoughts were a given that I was going to share regardless of the group, I had found my way in with all the villagers of Haasilgaon.

As it happened, Devjeet was now planning to return to his college. He had become somewhat of my bodyguard when outside the village and of course, he had been the coordinator of my travel to and from the village. I was a little worried about his leaving frankly, as I knew Mohanlalji was a busy man and he travelled from place to place for quite a bit of time and had a reputation for being away for long stretches of time, attending function after function given his stature in the community. While Devjeet had become too persistent a help, he was truly responsible for getting me acclimated with the surroundings.

He left that evening and I returned back to the farm with Mohanlalji, I knew that the next morning my regular routine for the village was going to start. I wasn't sure how many days I'd continue as my appointment in Bangalore with Romeshbhai was coming up soon but there was a part of me that was feeling like I didn't want to go. I had let my instincts take me so far, perhaps it was fitting then that the plans I had made to meet Sri Sri were not going to happen. Whether it was a miscommunication or simply an overextended promise that he wasn't able to fulfil, I found out that the dates I was to go to Bangalore weren't possible as Sri Sri had changed his travel plans and was not going to be there.

Speaking to Mohanlalji about this, he asked if I still wanted to make the trip to Shimoga. I wasn't sure, as I had just barely started the routine in the village. I asked if it was okay that I refrained for a bit and tried to set up a routine in the village for some time and then make a decision. He quickly reassured me that I need not ask the question and promised me not to ask it again, ever. He told me that this was my home and I need not ask his permission to stay.

I agreed to stay back and he seemed elated at my decision. I knew I had looming scans but at this point as I was feeling okay, I was willing to wait a few weeks to focus my attention on my treatment. Mohanlalji immediately began to suggest I meet certain people and go to certain places with him as I intended to stay. I agreed, as I knew each experience I was having was a first and I was enjoying learning from what felt like a whole new world for me.

The next morning, my routine began. I woke up at my usual 5:00 am, stepped outside my room and headed to the terrace directly above. I started to do my pranayama's and followed it with some *asanas*. As I then made my way through the farm, I'd stop and grab my morning leaves. What started as a short walk within the property led me to the end of the farm. I thought I'd walk along the main paved road. As I walked down listening to my ipod, I thought about how lucky I was to be able to breathe the clean air and get to witness the beautiful sunrise over the plains. I'd stop in my tracks as the sun would rise and do my *surya namaskar* pose before making my way back to the *gaushala*.

I'd head over, wish the cows a good morning and wait for Ganga or Gauri or Sakhshi to offer me their *gaumutra*. My time at the hospital had given me my voice back and I found in the *gaushala* my own personal stage where I'd sing along to my music or just hum. I noticed that the cows always enjoyed the music. It also seemed to expedite their giving me my *gaumutra*. That day Ganga offered it to me and upon collecting it, I made my way back to my room.

I had my morning leaves and *gaumutra* alongside a morning *upma* breakfast, then packed my clothes, preparing for the trip to have my bath. That day Mohanlalji had already left for the grape farms for some work. Rather than wait for his return, I ended up walking to Manavji's. It hadn't seemed very far when we would drive to and from the village, but Ajay and his family were uncertain that I'd manage the walk. I ended up getting a ride from a friend of Mohanlalji who had come to see him, but rather than taking me directly to Manavji's home, I told him to drop me off on the main road. It was a pleasant stroll from there via the banana trees to his home.

As I walked the path I had gotten to know, thanks to Devjeet biking me there back and forth, it didn't feel strange. In fact, having control and being able to travel without depending on anyone felt like a welcome change. Manavji seemed upset that I had walked but I told him that I needed to. After my bath and having my milk, I suggested to Manavji that I walk to the village. He seemed confident at this point given that I was still doing well. Knowing that Mataji's home came midway between Manavji's home and the village, I had a pitstop if needed.

I walked my way down the hill where Manavji's home sat atop, made my way towards the main road and headed towards the village. I got some interesting stares from curious bikers that passed by and knew who I was, they even offered me a ride. I frankly felt less pain walking then sitting on the back of the bike so I politely refused. In no time, I was at Mataji's place where Mohanlalji happened to be as well.

They both seem unamused that I had walked so much but as I assured them that I had enjoyed it, Mohanlalji felt some bit of relief. In a way, the tough conditions and the lack of conveniences was forcing me to challenge myself and I was going to embrace the word 'adjustment' as Mohanlalji had forewarned me before coming to Haasilgaon.

As Mataji went to fetch a plastic chair for me to sit on, I gave her a little lecture about her own health. Mohanlalji had shared with me that she refused to move from her home. She didn't mind the way they were living, despite Mohanlalji's offer for them to live in better and cleaner conditions either in the village or at his new farm. But Mataji had a routine. It was evident to me that ultimately that's what saved her life. Having seen her medical records, she had fought an aggressive battle. But the discipline in her life, while not what the hospital would have recommended, suited her. Frankly, seeing Abbaji, he was in a far worse condition that Mataji. Of course, attitude has a lot to do with health too. While Abbaji was a stoic man with little to say but plenty to complain about, Mataji seemed focused on her daily work and the isolation she had living on the farm provided her a semblance of peace. It dawned on me that my stay at the farm was also doing the same thing for me.

As I continued towards the village, I told Mohanlalji that I wanted to walk. It was my first walk into the village. As I made my way, I saw a bevy of school kids walk their way towards the school and school buses that would pick them up from nearby Mataji's home. I saw Shruti and her classmates. Her friends seemed excited to meet me. They were a little surprised that I was walking but I told them that I enjoyed it. Her friends then invited me to come over

to their home whenever time permitted. They wanted me to
meet their families. I agreed and said that I'd coordinate
with Shruti to set up a time.

From the distance, I could hear Amrut yell out for me.
He and Aayan were lagging behind Shruti and they
too seemed curious that I was walking my way to the
village. I told them that I enjoyed it. As an SUV horned
its way past us, I saw Amoljeet and Pranak, they were
students at a neighbouring village's private school.
Amrut and Aayan attended the local Haasilgaon Kannad
School while Shruti was at the local Marathi school.
Because of the location of the village, there was a choice
of either school in either language. As Haasilgaon
was literally 3 kms away from the Maharashtra border
and the village housed a large number of former Marathi
armed forces members, there was a significant
Maharashtrian influence, but the majority of labourers
and workers were Kannad.

Amrut and Aayan suggested I go with them to their
school. Amrut seemed determined to take me wherever he
went like a permanent show & tell display I told him in
good time, I'd visit his school. I told them to continue on as
I walked my way further into the village. I passed the bank,
it was actually a co-op bank named after Mohanlalji's
deceased first-wife. As they noticed me, the bank manager
Prakash invited me inside. He cleared everyone else out of
his office as I was introduced to the staff. It seemed
wherever I went, I realized that Mohanlalji's influence was
clear. Prakash had built a home opposite where Mataji
stayed. I had passed it many times but not realized it was
his home. There was a certain polish and urban feel to his
home, which upon chatting with Prakash, I realized came
after he had spent some time in Pune.

Seeing that he had returned and was now living in Haasilgaon, hoping to improve the situation of his village and fellow villagers, I was happy to see this full circle in effect. It was a strange thing to be living in a village where most of the local residents had left the area and spent years studying, working and serving and then decided to return back to their hometown. I had so often read stories of families shifting to cities for opportunities but it seemed that in the present landscape, folks were now coming back to their own land. Despite perhaps the loss of economic growth, they were content in living a simpler and according to me from what I had seen so far, a healthier life.

I headed to Sanjay's office after my time at the bank and got to meet some of Sanjay's students. They were college students but also working for Sanjay's BPO. It was interesting to meet the youth generation. As I shared with them the tales of my college days, it was such a disconnect. It's only then that I realized that many of these young men were less interested in a career and found more joy working on the farmlands, riding tractors and bikes. When I asked them what they aspired for, it was nothing more than some pocket money for their mobile phones and perhaps some additional clothes.

I'd always been surrounded by ambitious people wanting and willing to sacrifice parts of their lives to get something or go somewhere. Yet here in Haasilgaon, these young men were willing to accept the simple life even at their impressionable age. So even if they left Haasilgaon, it was clear they'd all find their way back home. After all, even Prakash and Sanjay, two success stories and points of pride for the village had come back.

As I mulled over this thought, I wondered if India was my coming back. Wouldn't coming back mean that India was my home? Over time, I had lost the concept of what it meant to feel at home. I was comfortable everywhere. In the span of just a few days, I was even feeling at home in Haasilgaon, living on a farm, surviving in a simple world where literally everybody knew my name (or my nickname).

As I returned home, back to the farm that night, I had some news. The labourer who had been living in the kitchen with his family had moved out. It was finally time for me to start up the kitchen. In addition, Mohanlalji confirmed to me that the bathroom had been cleaned up and that if I wanted to, I'd now be able to bathe there.

I was excited. I was finally going to be able to make the farm my home. Sure I'd go to the village and spend time with everyone there, but the increased sense of personal responsibility coupled with the ability to now stay back on the farm throughout the day, excited me. I never thought I'd be the sort of person to walk over to cows, pee outdoors and then go fill my drinking water from the well a while away and feel at home—yet my routine was getting instilled in me—and I knew that there was a lot of healing happening alongside it.

CHAPTER 16

Cow Cocktail

Har Ghadi Badal Rahi Hai Roop Zindagi;
  Every clock changes the colour of life
Chaon Hai Kahi Hai Dhoop Zindagi;
  There's shade some places and there's sun some
  places in life
Har Pal Yahan Jee Bhar Jeeyo;
  In every moment here, live life to the fullest
Jo Hai Sama Kal Ho Na Ho;
  For whatever time is there, may not be   there tomorrow
['Kal Ho Na Ho' by Shankar-Eshan-Loy]

Routine is a part of life we tend to forget unless we are
bound by it. In many ways, the routine I had created for
myself in the village was nothing less than a necessity.
Without it, I would have been lost and possibly would not
have had a purpose. While no one was 'checking up' on me,
I did feel a sense of obligation to make sure that the
purpose behind my stay was always front and centre.

Now that my morning routine was possible by just
staying on the farm, it permitted me to have a greater sense
of autonomy. As I woke up that morning, I realized that
something had changed. I was now in control of my day in
a way that had not yet happened. Between getting used to
the land, the space and the people plus not knowing about
the longevity of my stay—now I was about to start
something and there need not be an end date. I didn't have

one. I knew eventually I'd need to leave the village for my scans but at that moment my complete focus was going to be living in the moment and letting my routine dictate my life.

4:30 am like clockwork, I would be up and ready. I'd walk outside my room, head to the terrace and begin my meditation. After that I'd do my yoga and then put on my sneakers and head for my walk. After a conversation with Mohanlalji, I was encouraged to walk along the road path if I wanted. That morning I decided to do just that and walked my way to the village. It was just about 5 kms. I noticed several of the villagers too going for walks at that time. Each one stopped to chat and I quickly realized that it might not be the best route if I wanted to maintain one speed. As I made my way up the village and turned around, I stared to speed up. It wasn't forced but the pace was natural.

I realized there was a bonus to jogging. Between my heightened speed and listening to music, I could get away with just waving and go past people without having to stop or break my focus and speed. I ended up jogging halfway back to the farm then something in me decided to speed up further and I ran the remainder of the distance.

I stopped by the well to catch my breath, turned to the side and peed. I then walked over to the well and drank some water. It was a strange thing, I actually felt like I was a different person. I never ran, had never just dropped my shorts and peed outdoors and drunk water straight from the pump. Yet the whole routine felt normal. As I looked towards the pomegranate farms, I noticed the sun was just about to rise. I rushed back up to the terrace, removed my shoes and did my *surya namaskar* pose.

161

From the terrace I could see that my greatest cheerleaders, the cows were getting up. I quickly made my way to the *gaushala* wishing them all a good morning. Sakhshi seemed to be rather upbeat that day. She was an absolutely gorgeous cow. Black and white like a traditional jersey cow but her fur was so soft and her eyes simply sparkled. I had been taking pictures of the sunrise and the land and had taken some pictures of the *gaushala*, but that morning I was wearing a black undershirt and white shorts. Sakhshi and I were matching. I decided to take a picture of the two of us. While I knew the other cows wouldn't dare let me pose with them, Sakhshi was another story. She was striking poses and looking straight at the camera.

It was a bizarre feeling but I felt this connection with her that was clearly beyond words. Perhaps I was projecting but she reminded me of Mom, beautiful, gentle and most of all nurturing. She never spoke back and she liked being part of the group but shied away from the limelight. Yet for me, she shone in that *gaushala*. As I clicked away, I heard the all-too-familiar sound of *gaumutra* coming out. I quickly ran for the container and Ganga blessed me for the morning. I got as much as I needed and thanked her.

Ganga was a much tougher cookie to convince. She didn't not like me, but it took her time to get warm. Ajay had showed me that the way to her heart was through massaging her. I had seen him and Ajji do this and that morning I followed suit. Immediately she settled down and in fact, when I went to massage her neighbour Gauri, she got very upset and literally moved her body all the way towards me to have me continue. Ajay had mentioned she was having some pregnancy discomfort, she was about seven months in at that time. Clearly the massages were helping. It was one of the most satisfying experiences to give her a healing touch, the same way she was actively healing me.

As I realized it was time for my breakfast, I made my way out of the *gaushala*. I scooped up the top of the gobar, the part I'd need for my gobar bath and said goodbye to the gang. Sakhshi looked my way and I couldn't help but look back at her and smile. I walked my way to the kitchen. It was basically an empty room with a fridge and stovetop. The fridge was empty, as electricity was a much bigger problem than I had expected.

While there was an invertor, the fridge did not work on it. Additionally, the invertor only had enough juice for a few hours. As it turned out, despite the rains, there were blackouts that lasted six, eight, twelve, eighteen hours. It wasn't so much of a challenge given that there was little need during the day. But at night, it was necessary. As I started the kitchen that day, I knew I would need to change the timings of my meals, especially dinner.

I wanted to adhere back to the hospital timings for meals. The *'chauviar'* diet was something practiced by many Jains and all of us patients at the hospital. As I had done a little research on the topic while in Gujarat, I began to understand the practicality of it. It didn't strike me quite as clearly until that day. Without electricity and in the dark, to prepare the food, cook and eat it—there was something rather unhygienic about it. Living on a farm with countless bugs and animals around, it was important to actually see the food that I was eating. I wasn't comfortable, especially given my health, to eat food without knowing what I was consuming.

That it aided my digestive system and kept my stomach light for my morning treatments were added plus point. But there was something particularly wonderful about preparing my meals on the farm. My whole life I had prepared my meals and whatever scraps, waste and the food I wasn't going to consume, I'd throw away or it would go down the garbage disposal. As I looked out the window from the kitchen and saw the *gaushala*, those ends of tomatoes and onions or banana peels and rotis, I knew what was to be done.

I remembered something I had heard at the hospital, how so many city street cows eating garbage would end up eating plastic and other waste not suitable for their bodies. The question was asked, if we are praying to the cows and referring to them as *Gaumata* should we give them old, spoilt, rotten food? Is it not our responsibility then to give them fresh food? I thought, having just chopped the fruits and vegetables, why dispose it in a bag and wait for it to be spoilt and bacteria's form, when I could simply walk over right then and there.

So that too became part of my routine. Before I'd eat, I'd walk over to the cows and give them my scraps and a little of what I was having (if suitable). Of course I'd sometimes have to sneak in, as they'd all want to have it. But being one person making single servings, I wasn't preparing large meals. Sakhshi was my go-to as she was the first in line and generally didn't gloat about these things. Ganga and Tulsi would often fight over the food and as much as I didn't want to play favourites, everyone in that *gaushala* knew that she was special to me. While Ganga was my physical saviour—the emotional and spiritual connection that I had with Sakhshi was something much deeper.

As I went to have my breakfast, I saw Mohanlalji notice me. He was curious as to what I was having. I had made upma, but it was very different than what Ajji had been bringing us in the days past. I had used different oils and spices, chopped several vegetables and made it into quite a lavish breakfast.

It was interesting to see how and what quantity of food people ate in the village. Rice and roti was a staple, while vegetables and *dals* were more like condiments. As a child I too preferred this, but with age, I began to be more satisfied with the latter. As a patient in particular, it became that much more important.

Access to fresh fruits and vegetables was limited for the villagers, they attempted to grow it on their own lands even though it was a challenge. The village square had its own market set up on Saturdays, where vendors would come to sell, and as I was setting up the kitchen, I made my first trip there. Rakhee Didi suggested I go with Shruti, Amrut immediately jumped at the chance to go along as well.

As we made our way through the village, Aayan, Amoljeet and Pranak all joined me. On our way to the market, I realized the bizarreness of the situation. Here I was, the sole male with several young boys, walking around and purchasing vegetables. My eyes would go directly towards the *palak* and *methi* and other green vegetables. I was shocked at how cheap the cost was, but again, it made sense given the location. As I loaded my reusable tote, I had the good fortune of having little helpers to carry the weight, as they walked me from vendor to vendor, many of whom were their classmates. They were happy to have me there and suggested I take their tomatoes or onions or garlic. I happily complied but they'd refuse to take any money from me. It was an interesting feeling. Having come from so far away, I was an exotic creature for them, having lived a life of excess and wealth. I was first a guest of the village and they wanted to greet and treat me as such.

I saw what many of the Bhabhi's were buying and I realized they too were buying just about the same quantity. I spotted Kavita Bhabhi who asked to see what all I had bought. It was interesting; she was buying for a total of twelve people (including me) while bought for one. Yet our bill and the amount of vegetables were the same. Was I really consuming the same amount of vegetables as an entire family?

Amoljeet, Pranak, Amrut and Aayan took turns holding my market purchases, we walked pass fresh *kanda bhajjis* being deep-fried. It had been a long time since I was near anything oily, but one of the BPO college students happened to be preparing them. He insisted I try it and as I saw the look on all the boys' faces, it was clear that they were ready to enjoy this treat as well. I ended up getting two plates for all of us to share. And so this too became a part of my routine.

As I walked with the boys back to Mohanlalji's village home, I felt like the town celebrity, with his entourage. Many women came out of their homes watching me and laughing. I had amused them as they perhaps they had never seen a man spend this much time off the farmland focussing on food.

On my return I requested the boys to have Mohanlalji bring the bag with him to the farm, as I was planning on walking back that afternoon. They were surprised that I'd want to go back by foot but I knew I wanted to and the weather was perfect.

They escorted me up to Mataji's place where I stopped and checked in on how she was doing. As I told her about my day, she seemed truly excited that I was making myself at home. She also seemed happy that I was spending time with the boys and giving them some purpose. I told the boys I'd head back from there. They wished to come but I warned them of the length of the trip and we planned to do a leisurely walk to the farm another day.

I put on my headphones and headed back. By the end of that day, I had walked, jogged and run over 25 kms. That long distance too became part of my routine. I reached home, quickly made dinner, went to the cows to serve them, milked myself a glass from Ganga and then offered a prayer as I sat on the terrace watching the sunset.

I walked back to the *gaushala* and then went on to massage all the cows one at a time. I could see as I made my way down the line that Sakhshi was not happy that I was neglecting her. Still, she had to wait patiently as I wanted to thank them all. As it got darker, I noticed Ganga and Gauri both opting to sit down. By default, Sakhshi's turn got moved up. I stood by her and started to lightly massage her.

I don't know why but I started to talk to her about my day. It was a strange thing for me to be speaking aloud to an animal, yet it felt so natural. I truly felt like she was listening to me.

I sat down in front of Sakshi, where I was near her face after putting on some music, which happened to be a Bollywood playlist. I started to sing along and as always she seemed to enjoy my performance. As if on cue, the *'Kal Ho Na Ho'* title song started to play.

I had already seen so much history with the song. From that being the last song I remember Dad say he truly loved and how much he wished people would embrace the lyrics of the song to singing that song at the hospital and becoming the first introduction to so many of my new friends in India. And now this intimate moment with these animals who had done as much if not more for me than any family—this was special.

I got emotional and for the first time since my breakdown in Mumbai, I cried. However there was a big difference in the tears running down my face now. These were tears of contentment. I was happy. I was in the moment. I was finally shedding myself of all the layers I had built up to protect myself, to stay alive and positive. I was able to stand in front of these cows and strip myself of any judgment. In that instant, I saw Mom in Sakhshi. As a tear rolled down Sakshi's face, she looked at me with the same expression Mom had just a few hours before she passed away, when she had had a temporary awake moment from her weeks in a relatively comatose state. I knew that with each tear shed, something was leaving my system and would now not return.

I had spent so much time worried about the physical illness that had consumed my life. I didn't realize another cancer had spread for far too long, the one that got poisoned further by others, the one that almost made me give up on myself. Yet as I looked at Sakhshi and she at me, the world felt right. I was meant to be here, I was meant to meet her and in all the healing I had sought—I was getting a cure for this cancer.

CHAPTER 17

Dr. Do-A-Little or Dr. Do-A-Lot

So I made up my mind
I'll be around for a while
You can bet on your life
I'll be around for a while
['I'll Be Around' by Empire Of The Sun]

It's not every day that a terminal cancer patient is walking tens of kilometres from farms to villages and back. While I found it a completely normal progression—it was a sight to be seen. I'd come across various village women making their way to and from the fields for work. I was still just learning Kannad but it was clear that they were talking about me because I was able to understand the word 'American'.

One of the women managed to flag me down in the morning. She asked me why I was walking to another village and not Haasilgaon. I began to explain how I enjoyed exploring and had gotten bored of the same route every day. She suggested I take a ride rather than walk my way around. I told her I wasn't doing it for a purpose other than the fact that I wanted to do it. She seemed confused as to why I'd willingly want to walk as they themselves had no choice and had to. It was an interesting observation. While the villagers were busy upgrading their lives from walking to bikes to cars, I was going back to basics. Every household was decorated atop with a satellite dish and

169

every person had a mobile in hand. It was a very different village experience than what I would have had just a few years before.

But some things seemed frozen in time. Perhaps as a result of my increased mobility, my never-ending love-hate affair with plastic chairs and my mandatory bike rides (especially if raining, late at night or having to go to another village for a function), the one area of my body that was paining more so than before, was my back. While I tried to fight it, sometimes the pain was too strong and for too long. I had given up all painkillers. I wasn't going to veer in the wrong direction again—not this time.

I had been asking Mohanlalji if there was any one that did massages or any type of touch related therapy. Upon inquiring, an old man from a neighbouring village made his way to the farm to visit me. He looked like he was eighty years old and beyond skinny. I almost started to laugh thinking was he going to massage me or I him? He was a tailor by day and a volunteer masseur by evening. He didn't charge for his services but would accept whatever he was given. I was told not to worry about it as his massage money went straight to buying *desi* alcohol.

He and I went to the terrace of the farm, he had me remove my shirt and then started putting pressure on different parts of my back. Within a minute he had pushed me in so many different ways, I was beginning to wonder what the hell I had agreed to. He called for Mohanlalji and told him that he'd be able to help and then showed him exactly where my tumours were. It was frankly shocking for me to see how spot on he was in accurately knowing where the pain had originated from and he assured me he'd be able to help. He took out a small bottle of oil from his kurta pocket and rubbed it into my back. Over the next ten minutes, he massaged and applied acupressure to my back in a way that had I not consented, it would have been considered an assault. Yet as he got up and said he was done, I felt an immediate relief. I was hooked on this tailor/masseur.

I thanked him and from that day forward made it a point to see him three times a week. While he struggled to bike his way to me, I ended up visiting him on my afternoon walks. It added 6 kms to and from my routine and helped me to explore another village and make many more local friends along the way.

One such friend had wanted to meet me for quite some time. As had become commonplace at the hospital, once the news spread about my illness, my treatment and now me; I became a liaison/surrogate doctor for the locals. I wasn't sure if Mohanlalji himself had been touting this as he was the first line of contact for most. He'd then ask me if I'd be willing to speak and meet with them and suggest options for their disease. Given full well that my knowledge far exceeded that of those who were seeking my help—I agreed, with the disclaimer, that I was only in a position to share information and give my opinion.

As it turned out this opened the floodgates and friends, contacts and friends of contacts approached me to discuss their medical history and details. I was happy to do it but as I met patient after patient, I began to realize how little people actually knew about their disease and their overall health.

I tried to explain things but often times it didn't matter, they weren't looking for guidance, they simply wanted answers. I was unwilling to take the responsibility of making that decision for a patient. I expressed my hesitation to Mohanlalji but he seemed convinced that even my biased opinion was likely more educated and beneficial to the patient and family than anything they did on their own.

The trust Mohanlalji had in me in terms of my medical decisions was something that genuinely touched me. I had spent so much time, energy and effort in having to defend my choices rather than simply be happy with the fact that I was making a decision, no matter what. Mom had had that faith in me about her medical decisions when she was a patient and I particularly remember an appointment we had with her general physician just a couple of months before she died. I knew that the odds were stacked against her after yet another disappointing scan. The oncologist while optimistic had finally faced defeat and said that the chances of improvement were now mounting against us.

As the oncologist left the room and Mom managed to muster the words that, 'I'm not going to get better, am I?' I had two choices. I could have said 'yes you are', but instead I chose the truth, I said, 'probably not'. So when we visited her GP and I wanted to have a conversation about DNR (do not recessitate), it wasn't awkward. Mom and I had had many discussions about the end of life, particularly as an after effect of Dad's sudden death. She had been very clear in stating that she didn't want to live by any artificial support. I too agreed to the same principle. So when the time came for her to decide her fate and take advance directive on her fading life, Mom signed off and in full consciousness took steps to avoid any confusion as her health deteriorated.

Having taken similar steps for myself while preparing to come to India, I too had been ready for the end. As I shared this with other patients, it was no surprise that most were simply unwilling to hear this truth. They may have come to see me to help them find their cure, but I was going to make sure that they didn't continue to live in a world of denial and turn a blind eye to their impending reality.

Perhaps upon hearing this Mohanlalji refocused his attention on Mataji who had simply stopped all treatments from Laxmiprasad at this point. While she didn't show signs of any prevailing issues other than age related concerns, Mohanlalji suggested it was time for Mataji to get her scans. I too needed to get my scans but as a result of my insurance, my visa status and also some of my belongings still being in Mumbai, it made more sense for me to make the trip there and to handle all those matters together.

We went to the hospital to see Mataji's oncologist. It was the first time I had stepped foot into a hospital as a cancer patient in India. While the visuals of the patients and the desperation of the family members matched up to Laxmiprasad, there was one stark difference. The individuals sitting here were putting their complete trust in the medicine they were taking. I saw that same belief in Mataji who frankly had only a small leaf of it in the cow therapy because of me.

Mohanlalji invited me to join him and Mataji to meet her doctor. Rushed into a room as Mataji's case was considered VIP (courtesy of Mohanlalji's connections), we met the doctor who simply asked some questions to which she answered yes or no. I waited for some order to be given for a scan of some sort, but he concluded the 'exam' and said she was fine. It was a strange thing to witness as I was so used to my three monthly routine check-up including one or many scans.

As Mohanlalji introduced me to the oncologist, I had to ask him why he wasn't planning to do any tests with Mataji. He insisted that without pain or any symptoms it was simply not worth the money for Mataji to be tested.

I hadn't ever heard that answer being given by a doctor. It made sense but having lived through rounds of cancer, it just seemed like the wrong answer.

I professed my hesitation with the doctor and urged Mohanlalji that Mataji should get a scan, but he too seemed at peace with the oncologist's assessment. It was then that I realized that despite the inspiration I may have been for him—I wasn't getting through to him.

On the car ride back to the village I wondered about my own health. It had now been more than four months since I had been in India. So much had transpired in that duration of time. I clearly wasn't ready to die and my body seemed to be improving but should that be enough to trust that things were working? As I got home and walked over to Sakhshi, I got my answer.

In all the time I had spent so far in Haasilgaon and the farm, so much had changed in my life. I was breathing different air, eating different food, drinking different water, exercising, meditating, yoga, massage, village kids—you name it—I was l a completely different life than I had ever lived before. Did I need proof that this was the right decision? While my heart knew I was on the right track, my head needed the proof. First, I needed to know that this wasn't some extended high phase before I was still set to die. Second, I needed the evidence to prove to myself that I had in fact made the right decision to stay back in India and leave the world I knew behind. Finally, I needed the proof to assure myself that the cancer had not spread anywhere else. Having seen Mom and so many patient friends as they metastasized and knowing that the last place it would reach is the brain. I was unwilling to stay in India and let anyone other than paid, trained professionals care for me—I deserved that at the very least.

I told Mohanlalji that I needed to make the trip to Mumbai. He offered to have someone join me but I knew I needed to make the trip alone. I was to take a bus from the closest city to us, Chandraprabha, the overnight trip would have me in Mumbai by early morning. I had called Meena Chachi and Sapna Massi to inform them that I was making the trip. They were both somewhat excited, somewhat surprised. While both were interested in seeing me, neither mentioned, suggested or cared to ask where I was planning to stay. So as to save them face, I told them upfront that I was going to stay in a hotel as I had pending work in town and it would be most convenient.

Mohanlalji and Mataji were a little concerned but I reassured them that after having gotten this far, what could go wrong? And even if it did, I now had a place and a family who truly made it feel like home.

CHAPTER 18

Scantastic!

I Strong hand thick skin and an open heart
You saw through the pain saw through the mask
You never gave up on me yeah
Life life
From the coma
The wait is over
You loved me back to life life
['Loved Me Back To Life' by Celine Dion]

Returning to Mumbai after almost three months felt a little strange. So much had transpired I wasn't sure what the response would be by my relatives—would I even want to share my experience with them?

In my conversations over the phone it was evident that there was no physical room for me at any of their homes. They wished to see me, offering me a meal but the limits were set. I made arrangements to stay at a medium priced hotel, a far cry from where I used to stay. But after living in Haasilgaon, given that the room had a clean bed, electricity and running water in the bathroom—I was more than content.

Time had indeed passed by. The relatives that had so warmly greeted me and encouraged me to keep fighting and try different things seemed to have moved on from my topic and my life. I was still in their discussions but it was more about gathering information not giving inspiration.

I don't think there was ever a time in my life when I couldn't just call and go over to a relative's home, but things had changed. I had changed. There were reservations on both sides. Curiosity and an overall sense of apathy strained the relationship. Without a return date back to America, even a one-night invite could unknowingly become a much longer commitment on their part.

It's funny. In the past, we'd extend our trips because we were having such a good time and now, before I came, they wanted to know when I was leaving. But at this point, none of that mattered. I was here with a purpose and my purpose was to get my scans done and to see if the improvements that I felt in my day-to-day village life were amounting to anything in my scans.

The news turned out to be better than I could have expected. While I was almost certain that it hadn't spread further, I was surprised that the PET-Scan showed almost zero detection of cancer in my lungs now, with the tumours in my liver and stomach having decreased a little and my spine at about the same level.

This was inspiring news and I knew that I was going to book the very next bus back to Haasilgaon. While I had already been content in my routine, this further reaffirmed my dedication. All the doubts I had about the longevity of staying there disappeared, except for one thing—the temporary stability. Upon returning home I got my answer without having ever really asked the question.

The Mumbai weather, pollution and the overall chaos of the trip had taken its toll on me physically. Upon returning, I fell quite sick. It wasn't anything severe but given my compromised immunity and my self-reliance on day-to-day tasks at this point, for taking care of my needs (except washing my own clothes), I was truly living independently.

I had made a deal with myself that it was okay to have lunch in the village, as I spent this time with the many Bhabhi's kids. Being in the village through the afternoon gave me an opportunity to give back and I got one meal made for me.

On that particular day my back acted up and a familiar friend from the past—pain—made a dramatic reappearance that day. My body was simply unable to handle most of the things I was used to in my routine. Devjeet had been visiting and I told him that I'd not be able to come into the village, even on a bike. He offered that he'd have Mohanlalji bring me a tiffin lunch from home, so I need not worry. As the day went by and Ajay and his family went to the fields, I was literally alone on the property. Even my screams would go unheard.

I kept looking at the clock, time was going by and no one had returned. I tried to call up but Mohanlalji's phone was switched off (this was often the case as too many people were trying to reach him at all times and hours). I knew there was nothing much in the kitchen so I decided to stop worrying and just simply take rest. Devjeet made his way back to the farm at about 4:00 pm. As he came in to see me, he was shocked to hear that the food had not been delivered. He had just come back from somewhere else and had assumed that I had got my tiffin quite early on. Embarrassed by this slip-up he called up the house, who explained that no one was there or had come back so they had no way to send the food. I tried to calm down an angered Devjeet given that I wasn't really upset. Frankly I wasn't really even that hungry. I told him these things happen and not to worry.

However news travelled fast. There were seldom any visitors for me at the farm. My day always included a trip into the village. As Mohanlalji was always on the move, people didn't generally visit much unless with a specific purpose. But that evening, I had guest after guest. They had come to see how I was doing and to also bring me food. It was the village apology for something rather innocent that truly did not offend me.

As it turned out, I was feeling slightly better the next day and so as to not have another flood of visitors, I thought it best to toughen it out and head to the village to rest for the day at Mohanlalji's home. The bhabhi's were all truly sorry and wished me well. As they prepared my lunch (incidentally, it was a menu of my favourite dishes—not sure if they did that intentionally), I sat nearby on my plastic chair. The electricity was gone so thankfully there was no Marathi serial rerun from the night before to fight for attention with.

Geeta Bhabhi was the first to voice that she was very concerned for me. I told her that sometimes pain happens and I have to rest so as to avoid it getting worse. I apologised for causing this drama. They remained quiet. I then shared that my reports had come back better and that upon speaking to Mohanlalji, I was going to continue treatment in Haasilgaon. Without any prompting Roma Bhabhi, Mohanlalji's wife who had always been quite quiet till then, finally spoke up and said very proudly 'good'. I told them that my health was improving so they'd not have to worry about me as much and tried to make excuses for my minor health issue from the previous day. The three of them went on to say it's no worry.

Despite having the approval of all the villagers, Mohanlalji and even the cows, I needed these three women on my side. At the end of the day, I was adding work for them, and no one else. I didn't want to be the forced guest who became a burden. Having experienced this before I did not want to overstay my welcome. While I prepared myself to finally hear the truth and to know what these women really thought—I ended up getting schooled.

Geeta Bhabhi said that I should just stay there with them. Roma Bhabhi agreed. They then added I should just leave everything behind, get settled, marry and live a wonderful life there with them. I had been used to Mohanlalji speaking this way but coming from them—I was further touched.

It didn't surprise me that Kavita Bhabhi hesitated to join in. She was the rational one. Of the three women, she was the only original wife as the other two had passed away in that car accident. She had also been the one to manage the finances of their dairy business and buy the groceries. As the 'alpha' bhabhi, my added time there meant added expenses and a greater dip into their savings. While I had always offered to contribute, it was never accepted so I was left having to ensure that I was the added weight.

Again without prompt, Kavita Bhabhi said very matter of fact to me—'this place suits you—make it your home'. Hearing her say this, I was further surprised. I thanked all three of them but also wanted to reassure them. I said I'd only stay so long as my health was improving. I knew well enough that if I were getting better, the responsibility would lessen and not increase.

Roma Bhabhi jumped in and asked if I didn't get better, what was I planning? I told her that I'd go back to America and spend my remaining days in a nursing home. I didn't want anyone to have the burden of caring for me. In unison, they all asked what burden? I told them that I'm okay in Haasilgaon. I'm able to take care of myself but coming to the village for meals, the rides back and forth, people going out of their way for me when I needed something—I couldn't imagine that long-term.

I clearly got a bit emotional, I was already so grateful for this entire bonus chapter of my life. As I ate my tears, Geeta Bhabhi explained it best. She asked me who I had in America to take care of me. I told her that I had friends. She said, 'here you have family'. It wasn't the family she had heard me talk about—but rather it was the village. She said 'you have 2000 family members. How big a burden can you be to that many people?'

However I knew the reality and that the ultimate responsibility would fall on this family and in particular, these women's hands. Roma Bhabhi shrugged it off and asked 'why be so worried, we're all here'. Kavita Bhabhi then stepped in, 'we've taken care of each other our whole lives. This isn't obligation; this is what it's like here. You are one of us and we take care of our own, no matter what'.

And finally, just like that, in those three little words—'no matter what'—I truly let go of the fear of dying.

For the first time since my cancer had come back, I was in a place with people who cared enough. I knew no matter what was going to happen and now no matter when or what condition I was in—I'd be okay. That day became the day that I stopped carrying my return ticket to US in my pocket. I knew I wasn't going to end up like so many I had heard about or seen, like my *nani* who spent her final years tossed like a ball between her two son's homes (the third mama had no financial means to support her). Forever in my head is the vision of her tucked away in a room at the back of the house (or an enclosed terrace in the other house), seated in the dark, unable to really freely move around. She'd eat her meals alone despite a full family, her own full family in the same house.

I refused for that to be my end. The three bhabhi's assured me this would never happen while I stayed in Haasilgaon. For the first time in a long while I finally believed that to be true.

With the fear of death now behind me, it felt like I was finally ready to live. While I had learned to embrace each moment, I was now willing to live with a purpose. Perhaps this is really where my second life started—not bound by the end—everything was new and fresh and every experience now felt like part of a new story.

CHAPTER 19

V.V.I.P.

I had to go through hell to prove I'm not insane
Had to meet the devil just to know his name
['Ghost' by Ella Henderson]

It was 3:45 am. The weather had gotten slightly chilly on that autumn morning. Mohanlalji knocked at my door telling me it was time. He said that Ajay had heated the water and that I could take a bath if I wished. He had already gotten dressed. It felt like I was getting ready to catch an international flight—much like those early morning Air India flights my family and I used to take, back when I was a kid. But Mohanlalji and I were getting ready for a trip to a *mandir* that I jogged by every morning.

This morning was special though. A special *Babaji* was making his annual pilgrimage to the village, to share his insights on everything from politics to crops to the economy. The temple was overseen by the local Sarkar, a fading celebrity of the area who had seen his land and his influence diminish over the years but still managed to hold the respect and appreciation of the locals, who hosted this event. As a guest of Mohanlalji and as one of my daily walking friends, Sarkar enjoyed my company and invited me to witness the local tradition.

As I sat there in the cold watching the *Babaji* pray, dance and spew out predictions about the future, it felt like I was in a National Geographic special. But the scepticism that once would have derailed the experience for me, had changed to hope. While I looked into the eyes of the believers who had travelled from so far away to hear about the fate of their land—I wondered how close I was to being my own version of a *Babaji*.

Already being the American, the Doctor, the runner—I was now becoming the *Babaji*. While it started with the boys Amrut, Aayan, Pranak and Amoljeet, then the girls, Shruti and her friends, this fandom spread as I got invited to the schools. I had first visited Shruti's's school and then Amrut and Aayan's school on August 15th, Independence day. Shruti's school principal had invited me to be a guest lecture for the 8th, 9th and 10th standards.

I wasn't sure what I was going to talk about but she asked me to speak about America, India, the differences and then something inspirational. Given that my understanding of Marathi had improved, I still had a long way to go as far as speaking was concerned. She suggested I speak in Hindi but throw in some English. I couldn't believe I managed to hold their attention in my *'tutta-futta'* Hindi for a good hour. We then had a thirty minute Q&A session, which proved to be incredibly exciting as the inhibitions that had restricted so many students from asking interesting questions, when I visited their homes came to light here.

It was interesting to speak to young minds, willing to listen to every word and preserve what you had to say. I spoke to the young women of the class, similarly as I had done in some of their homes—hoping to enrich and encourage them to keep studying and not let their families settle them down quickly into marriage—I saw that the enthusiasm and appreciation I had for them was quite possibly the first time they had received that kind of empowerment. For me, it was something that proved that I was in Haasilgaon for a reason.

It was a great honour then to be asked to raise the flag on Independence Day at their school. While this distinction generally went to the usual list of local politicians and such—it was exciting for the kids but truly a proud moment for me.

August 15th was a busy day as I then went to Amrut and Aayan's school, where I assisted Mohanlalji with the flag hoisting. From there we proceeded to the neighbouring village, a girl's school where they asked me to speak after some speeches presented by them.

As I spoke to relatively younger girls, I shared with them my excitement about being with them at this moment in time. It seemed the optimism that was working its magic on my body and soul, was now helping my mind to focus and give meaningful inspiration to those who seldom hear it. I spoke to them about choices and why it was important for them to study. While I wasn't sure what necessarily stuck with them, from that day onwards, I knew I had given them some hope. If a boy from America could make his way to a rural village in Southern India, why couldn't a rural villager from that same place make their way to America?

This lingered with many of the students. I continued with this message over the course of several months during my stay in Haasilgaon. From other neighbouring schools including the private school of Amoljeet and Pranak to the local colleges—my message was spreading.

I returned back to the Marathi school more frequently than others, given it was directly on my way, when walking from the farm to the village. I started to feel a little less restricted and spoke to the students about history, agriculture and then a personal passion of mine—sanitation.

On one of my daily walks towards the village, I got curious as to why everyone felt the need to defecate on the main street coming into the town. Of course it was an old habit but with so many homes now having nearby bathrooms, why the continued acceptance. With Amrut and Amoljeet one day we started to count the number of faeces on the road. Between both sides, it totalled over one hundred and fifty. The boys were getting a kick out of this disgusting exercise. I was less bothered by the site and more appalled by the fact that many years of studying my own stool had me diagnosing each individual's ailments, without even knowing their identities.

Regardless, I used the exercise to make a point in my lecture. While most students were embarrassed to admit they engaged or were responsible for this, they all understood the point I was driving home. We have great respect for the Gods and our families (at least in Haasilgaon that was still the case), there is no respect for the land. And given that majority of their families were farmers who religiously prayed throughout the year to protect the land and make it fertile for their economic stability, they were literally defecating on the same land that was responsible for their survival.

This took me back to Sakhshi and the cows. How could I permit any injustice or be indifferent to them, when they were literally showering me with love and medicine. It humbled me when I returned home and heard the news that the *desi* cow that had provided milk to all the kids of Mohanlalji's family had died and the last rites were being planned. Unlike anything I'd ever seen before, the cow was cleaned, draped with a beautiful red sheet and then buried in the ground near the *gaushala*.

As I tried to understand this, Mohanlalji told me that having her nearby would be the greatest blessing for his land. It touched me to see such respect being given to an animal and that they knew how much she had given them. This was further reaffirmed when I saw Devjeet make a special trip just to pay his respects.

It was a bizarre moment of realization, and again proved something that my conversation with the bhabhi's had already done. If this love was bestowed upon a cow, I knew I would be comfortable making Haasilgaon my final destination.

As the weather got cool and everyone in the village started to get busy for Dusshera and Diwali holidays Rakhee Didi suggested I make a trip to visit her brother Amar in Goa. Given that it was a relatively short trip (about 4 hours), she thought it would be a nice change for me and I would enjoy a break from the daily routine.

I was a little hesitant given my strict daily schedule but I knew how well she cared and she assured me that I'd have a good time. Part of me wanted a break as well. I hadn't really seen or done anything other than focus on my health the entire time I was in India. Perhaps this would be my break.

I spoke to Mohanlalji and he thought it was a great idea and the next thing I knew, I was on my way there. The bus ride was beyond chaotic and arriving at a monsoony Goa was probably not the best idea. Yet, I somehow managed to reach, and Amar and I made our way around the city. He had his bike and I was weary of long rides, but for the first time in a long while, the pain wasn't lingering. I wasn't quite sure what I was expecting at his home. There was no bed and I had to sleep on the floor with just a blanket. I was of half mind to go right back, but I wasn't going to let it stop me from accepting this experience.

I truly thought my trip to Goa was going to be physically relaxing but in reality, it was quite the adventure. It turned out to be a great test for me. My stamina, endurance and ability had clearly improved. Amar even managed to get us access to a government facility that housed *desi* cows and I could have my daily fresh *gaumutra* every day.

It also opened up my eyes to the potential of being able to continue my treatment outside of Haasilgaon. While I had no plans to leave, it was an important thing to see that my survival (at least the treatment portion) was not reliant on one village.

The trip was short but it proved to be exactly what I needed and it also became more than what I expected. It was evident that village hearts extended well beyond the borders of Haasilgaon and that slowly but surely I was building a new network of family that wanted to be there for me and it wasn't out of obligation but out of love.

As I returned to Haasilgaon, I kept the momentum going. My meditations got longer. Yoga became more intense and extensive. My walks were turning more from walks and jogs to jogs and runs. My time with the kids proved fun and educational and I felt lucky to be welcomed by all those that came to see me whether for medical advice or anything else.

In my local 'celebrity' status, I was mindful not to forget one key thing. I was making Haasilgaon my home but I was still a guest because I was staying at Mohanlalji's farm. It was not something I wanted anyone to think I was taking for granted. While there was no monetary exchange for my time there, I made sure that I was contributing to the welfare of his property and doing whatever work was possible to support his growing business.

Whether it was simply staying back at the farm to show someone around, walking the farm to keep an eye for issues or educating the labour working in the fields—I had my little ways of trying to contribute. Mohanlalji never demanded anything of me and wanted me to focus completely on my health, but giving was part of my recovery and to not help him in whatever way I could just didn't sit well with me.

As it turned out, I got an opportunity, a rather unexpected one.

CHAPTER 20

The Miracle Worker

I love this life
But it only lasts a minute
And do you love this life
Cuz if you do I promise I can make it last forever forever forever
['I Love This Life' by Kim Cesarion]

My father always wanted me to be a doctor. That brisk November morning, as I literally straddled Abbaji and called his time of death, I wondered how my life had led me to a place where I was making medical decisions and having others not just listen to me but follow my instructions to the T, about how to care for their terminal loved ones.

It was just a little less than a month before Abbaji's death that Mohanlalji asked me to join him on a trip to Hillori. His father had been experiencing quite a bit of pain when passing his urine. A long-term diabetic with several complications, it justified his relatively grouchy personality (of course, it didn't excuse it).

We went to meet their doctor of choice, Dr. Wakde. I had met him before and he and I shared an understanding about my illness, he seemed quite supportive of the path that I was taking, so long as I was sure of the ramifications. I was, and I had the peace of mind · knowing that if something were to happen, there was at least an educated doctor nearby that I could connect with when needed.

To bring the focus back to Abbaji, it turned out that his complications now also included a last stage bladder cancer. Given his weak kidneys, his weak heart and his overall poor health, Dr. Wakde determined Abbaji to be in his final stage. A surgery was out of question so the best bet was painkillers and a peaceful goodbye.

It was shocking news for the family, given that a doctor would normally provide a sugar-coated answer, but I respected Dr. Wakde for telling the truth. Of course, possibly my presence and asking of specific questions may have prompted this but regardless, the point was that there were very limited options. In essence, now the family had to decide if it was better for Abbaji to come home and fight his remaining battle at home or as Dr. Wakde offered he could come to the hospital and they'd keep him as comfortable as possible.

It was not a surprise that after hearing such shocking news, Mohanlalji made the decision to hospitalize him. I of course voiced my thoughts, but knew no matter what age or condition, it's tough to accept such a bitter piece of news. I let go of my thoughts, but did advise Mohanlalji that the road ahead was going to be tough and its up to him to decide how much of a circus he wanted his father's last days to be.

As word spread about Abbaji's health and the irony that Mataji had just triumphantly returned from her cancer battle, the entire village made its way to see Mohanlalji and Abbaji. I made the daily trip to the hospital to check on him and was amazed how literally, from 7:00 am to midnight, there was a constant stream of visitors from every village within a 100 km radius.

I wasn't sure if it was the best thing for Abbaji, as his immediately family was more focused on serving *chai* and biscuits to those visiting, than to him. If there was one person that seemed focused on him, it was Devjeet. I finally managed to voice my concerns with him. I made it a point to be there, when Dr. Wakde would come for rounds, to ensure that whatever was relayed to him was the truth and not some false impression.

As his health went up and down over the coming few days, it was clear that despite all the advice and forewarnings I had given, little was being done to change the situation. I spoke to Mohanlalji in confidence and suggested that perhaps Abbaji will not be willing to die unless he's taken home. While he hesitated, the endless parade of visitors became more of an obstruction to the peace Abbaji needed to close his eyes, Mohanlalji finally agreed to bring him home.

Given that his two sisters had also arrived and the house had enough support to manage the visitors (who for the most part had already shown face, said their goodbyes and got credit for coming), finally the transfer back to the home was done.

It felt surreal to experience another family replicate first-hand the exact same thing I had done with Mom. Of course, the difference couldn't have been larger. When I had brought Mom home on Christmas Eve, I was managing a one-man show. I was doctor, nurse, cook, caregiver—everything. The next ten days that passed, had got more challenging but also gave me the opportunity to be a true son and do things that I never thought I would have to do.

That I got the opportunity again in Haasilgaon, despite the presence of literally thousands of people, told me something. I was no longer doing this for a reason; I was doing this because it was my calling. With his wife, five children, countless grandchildren and hundreds of neighbours and relatives around him—how I managed to be the one overseeing Abbaji's welfare—instructing them how to give him his medicines, telling them why not to feed him, showing them how to change his diaper to how to hold his hand to prevent infections to finally sitting atop of him and calling his time of death—I was meant to be there for this family at this moment in time.

While I had been prepared for Abbaji's imminent death, I was not prepared for what happened next. Manavji looked at me from afar to warn me not to say anything. He kept lying to everyone, a crowd growing by the second. He had to buy time to get the local doctor there. The local doctor was a Bachelor of Ayurveda medicine, technically not even allowed to administer an injection, yet he oversaw the welfare of most of the villagers in Haasilgaon. I had had previous encounters with him over Abbaji's last few days. Each time he came to check in, it seemed that I was filling in the family on what was happening and he simply agreed with me. So in that final moment, as he approached what was now simply Abbaji's body, I told him there was no pulse and stated the exact time. He nodded and the next thing I knew, I was literally lifted by Manavji as several men took Abbaji's body to the other side of the living room.

With that, the largest howl of cries I had ever heard started and what seemed like a stampede of women made their way into the living room. As Manavji airlifted me to safety outside, I could see that the entire village was focused and standing around Mohanlalji's home.

I wasn't quite sure how to handle what I was witnessing. Given that everyone had had over three weeks to say goodbye, they knew what was happening and had time to prepare—I didn't expect the mass hysteria that surrounded me. How much of it was genuine, how much for show or how much was simply a Pavlovian automatic response—I had no idea.

Whatever the case, from the silence of Mom's death to the isolation of Manish Mama's death to the beauty of the cow's death to now the absolute insanity of Abbaji's death—I had witnessed it all. Within just a couple of hours, it seemed like every person that had visited Abbaji over the last month made the procession along with us towards the riverbank, about 2 kms past Haasilgaon.

As Amoljeet and Pranak had been with me majority of the time, they had seen me caring for Abbaji. In his final moments, as his immediate family gathered around, I noticed both their faces and the confusion as they were trying to decipher exactly what was happening. Nobody seemed to be paying attention to their grief and they attached themselves to me. I walked with the two of them towards the cremation area.

Either side of us, was car after car, each one filled to the T with mourners. I wasn't sure if this was coming from love, respect or obligation but it took me to a place I thought I had stopped thinking about.

If I were to close my eyes in Haasilgaon, would this be what lay ahead? Of course I'd be dead and have no idea of what spectacle there was, but from the fear of dying alone and no one being there to pull the electric switch, now I wondered who out of the thousands would get that honour? I'd say Mohanlalji, but he had already done this for his wife, his son and now his father—did I need to add to his grief?

As it turned out, the very next day, many of Mohanlalji's friends came to see me at the farm. Mohanlalji was not allowed to leave his village home for the next thirteen days as tradition dictated. They came to check up on the labour at the farm and also requested me to keep an eye on things. I wilfully agreed as they explained to me that the next few days would be packed with visitors from all wakes of Mohanlalji's life. Concerned for his wellbeing it was the first time they asked me about my plans, not so much about my choice to stay and for how long but rather about in case of any emergency. It was a topic of discussion amongst Mohanlalji's friends but he never chose to ask me. Perhaps the intensity of Abbaji's death had them worried.

I mapped out for them my plan and thoughts on the matter. As it turned out, my fear was vastly different from their concern. While I thought they were concerned about how to help me or handle my financial situation in such a case, they were actually worried that given my American background and non-relationship with my family, would Mohanlalji get into trouble or be questioned. I told them no such issue would come about and they seemed content by my response. It frankly surprised me that my concerns were non-issues for them. I was so set in Haasilgaon, they were going to be there just as the bhabhi's had indicated—no matter what.

Perhaps motivated by having partaken in the final days of Abbaji, I got the strength to make some phone calls that honestly I had been avoiding. I had been in touch on and off with friends from Laxmiprasad hospital but with time, I began to get a little worrisome. While my health was improving, I knew that wasn't the case with everyone. I was always fearful to call, as I didn't want to receive any bad news about my friends, but as soon as I dialled the number for Rajeev—I predicted the worst.

As it turned out, I was right. Rajeev's sister answered the phone and immediately passed the phone to his mother. She couldn't stop crying as she informed me that Rajeev had indeed passed away after complications from a surgery, as his cancer had spread. I was deeply saddened but unfortunately not surprised. Over the years, I had gotten this news so often about the many wonderful people I had met along my cancer journey, yet each time it felt like an unfair jolt to my heart. She asked me how I was doing and I told her that I was still in active treatment and yes I was still following the cow therapy from the hospital. She tried to find a reason for everything we were enduring—I told her that there was no logic but at the day's end it was better for Rajeev to go. I knew how much pain he'd been in over the last few months. She agreed but simply could not let go of her son.

I thought about the many years preceding Mom's cancer that I had been sick. Each and every day despite my assuring her I was going to be okay, that wasn't the reality for her. For Mom, after losing her husband, the idea of losing her son—it's not something that can be easily accepted. I still wonder if her tumour would have developed without my illness. I had come across so many families where one spouse or parent had developed cancer, only for the other spouse or child to be diagnosed just a short time later. I was part of that statistic but I wasn't going to let that grief affect me anymore.

To prove my strength I continued with my calls. I spoke to Monali who had swapped treatments and after some unsuccessful additional alternative treatments had been forced to resort to allopathic medicine. I wasn't surprised but I was concerned. While her spirits were high and her humour still intact, her health was fading. She told me not to worry and I even spoke to her husband who reassured me that she would improve but it was something

I had heard before, yet I was in no place to be able to do anything more for her other than be her friend.

As the calls continued, the list of deaths, of patients I had met increased but there were a couple of shining exceptions. Alpesh uncle had improved significantly. Madhvi aunty was actually continuing the treatment at home with the same rigidity as we followed at the hospital. I then spoke to Neelam who also seemed upbeat about her mom, Ananda Massi. I got to speak to her and she was as chipper as ever. While there was still the occasional pain, she continued to the best of her ability the Laxmiprasad treatment at home. She was also mixing some allopathic treatments alongside, to ensure there was no issues and to minimize her pain.

As I exhausted my list of calls, I was glad I had finally gotten some updates. It wasn't the best of news but all of us at the hospital had met each other at crossroads. While we didn't know each other for long and hadn't spent enormous amounts of time together, the time spent was quality time, when we were at our most vulnerable. Similar to the friends I had made in the US during both Mom's journey and mine—these relationships were actually based on something. I needed to keep them alive because they were reminders of where I had come from and how far I had come.

Over the course of the next several days I met the who's who of the area, as droves of people dare I say thousands of mourners, made their way to Mohanlalji. On the fourth day, we made our way again to the river, this time with Abbaji's favourite foods in hand to feed to the crows.

It was a good sign for the deceased's soul if the crows came quickly to eat the food. As it turned out, despite circling the area for quite some time, the crows simply ignored the entire food spread. So as to entice the response they were hoping for, they brought a *desi* cow from a nearby farm to eat the food. The cow too seemed rather disinterested at eating it. After almost fifteen minutes, finally with some forced manipulation by his handler, the cow started having some of the food placed there.

On my way to witnessing the ceremony, I had thought the entire ritual was ridiculous. How does a crow eating the food quickly mean that Abbaji's soul is in peace? I had extended my spirituality well beyond what used to be my comfort zone, on my journey, but this seemed just too far-fetched. Yet as I saw the crows going round and round and then the cow doing the same thing—I was dumbfounded. Sometimes, you truly have to see it to believe it.

Abbaji was a grouchy old man in a lot of pain. Despite this reality, he was completely unwilling to let go and die in peace. He should have died in the hospital but he didn't. He came back to his home and even there pulled on far longer than he should have. He didn't die gracefully or in peace like Mom. Despite my convincing Mohanlalji and the rest of his family that he had passed away peacefully—it couldn't have been farther from the truth.

But witnessing such a gruesome death had forced me to once again think about the question that I had asked the Jain sadhus at the hospital—the connection between suffering and pain. Abbaji refused to accept his suffering with grace and as a result he endured a lot of pain, to the point that even after his death, all signs were pointing to the fact that his soul was still not ready to go.

Over the course of my time in India, I had heard so much usage of the word 'karma' to explain and justify any and all illnesses; I couldn't help but think it was a cop out. But as I embraced my new reality and opened myself up to the belief of karma—I wondered how karma and past life related to suffering in this life. The general argument was that we were paying the price of our past lives in this present life and thus a disease like cancer was had because of this.

For me, at this point in time, I had seen too much. I simply wasn't buying this thought because I had seen good and bad, rich and poor, healthy and unhealthy, young and old, American and Indian, you name it—I had seen, met and befriended every kind of cancer patient. To say that we were all simply victims of our karma, felt like we had nothing in our control.

Yet for me, perhaps Abbaji's death and these rituals shed light on something else. Maybe our karma was a pre-existing condition but once diagnosed, it was our character in this life that determined our kind and length of suffering. Both Mom and Abbaji ultimately had a very similar downward spiral in the last month. Yet while his suffering increased over the last month, Mom's was next to nil. Death and dying didn't need to be 'suffered'—it was pain that determined our suffering.

But pain is felt. I don't buy that karma determines our pain, it is our character in this life that determines our threshold. The more we tolerate and the more we accept, that too with a smile, was most likely going to result in greater peace. As I looked back at the many friends I had lost—this rang very true. Even for those who died quickly, many endured such great pain in their last few hours, who was to say that those last few hours of suffering wasn't more than the total pain Mom had endured during her entire illness.

As I realized this, the voice inside me strengthened further. If we were a sum of all of our experiences and our character determined our suffering—I knew now that I was okay. Karma threw what it wanted my way but my acceptance of it saved me. At every turn when I thought I was alone, I still had something—it was faith. Whether it was in a God or a stranger or a cow or in myself—I had enough trust in the universe—that I could manage any suffering and any pain. These were tests and at this point I was passing with flying colours.

CHAPTER 21

Holy Cow! Part 2

Nobody's perfect
Nobody's perfect
What did you expect
I'm doing my best
Nobody's perfect
Nobody's perfect
I was dishonest
I will do my best
['Nobody's Perfect' by Madonna]

Saying that the most important time of my day was spent literally with the cows—it was true transformation that if I had been viewing my own life from afar—I would still not have believed it. The *gaushala* was no longer just my refuge, it was my home.

Abbaji's death had left quite a spiritual impact on me and on the 13th day as the entire village came together to eat (so as to mark the end of the mourning period) and Mohanlalji, with a clean shaven head (as was tradition) welcomed everyone in, it was clear that he was more than ready for the spectacle to be over.

I had decided to stay back in Haasilgaon through the entire mourning period despite the fact that my next trip to Mumbai was pending for scans. I kept my routine going strong and the morning walks had converted into morning runs. I was surprised how dedicated I had become given that I never considered myself an athlete.

With little mirrors—simply enough to shave with and no weighing scale—I actually had no idea how significantly I had already transformed. When I left the hospital for the second time I weighed 86 kgs, it was just about 10 kgs less than when I had first come to the hospital. While I still felt uncomfortable removing my shirt at *gobar* time, I knew that I was significantly smaller than before.

In fact upon arriving at the village, I had first befriended the local tailor, I needed to request him to tighten all my pants and jeans since they were not staying up without a belt. Soon enough, I had him working on all my shirts and kurtas. Over the course of several months, I became his regular client coming in and getting clothes altered over and over again. But by January 2013, he said it was no longer possible with some of my clothes, they were just not going to be sized in anymore.

As it happened, we had gone to Hillori to see Dr. Wakde with Mataji, just to make sure she was okay after all the commotion of Abbaji's death. She had stopped the cow therapy just a month into my stay and all the heightened stress worried me, but thankfully, her reports came back clear. While there, I managed to find a weighing scale and my eyes couldn't believe what it reported—I was down to 75 kgs. I was blown away by the dramatic change that had transpired over the course of a year.

While I was off the steroids and clearly eating and living better—it was still a moment forever etched in my memory. For years, I thought I had tried everything to lose weight. I was never a dieter per se but someone who wished to be healthy, yet despite daily workouts at the gym and closer detail to food, I wasn't very successful. The most ironic part about my cancer was that I was looking forward to the weight loss but in reality, I actually gained weight due to the steroids. So coming to India and seeing the dramatic transformation of 25 kgs was truly unreal. I knew my upcoming visit to Mumbai would need to include visits to relatives—if not for anything else just to see if they'd recognize me.

There were many things that contributed to this loss. First and foremost, the stopping of the steroids but the continued shrinking of my tumours was the biggest contributor. After that, I knew it was the food I was eating—not just what I was having but when I was having it. The *chauviar* diet, per se, was working for me. Additionally, between my meditation, my yoga and my extensive walking (now running)—I was continuously mentally and physically engaged. Finally, I was happy—I couldn't remember the last meal I had where I hadn't smiled.

That day as we returned from our visit to Dr. Wakde, I went over to the *gaushala* and shared my news with the cows. Of course I wished to document the moment so I took another selfie with Sakhshi and as always she was more than ready to 'say cheese'. As I looked at the picture and saw myself, I realized there was one final thing that had contributed to my physical change—it was these cows. From the *gaumutra* and *desi* milk to their blessings in general, I was a different person because they had changed me from the inside.

The thought of actually leaving them behind for a few days to go to Mumbai was truly the most challenging part of leaving. I wasn't ready to go but I knew I needed to get yet another round of verification. Thankfully, it proved to be a short and successful trip.

While I was confident that my scans would show improvement, there was always a part of me ready to hear otherwise. The news was positive, no cancer detection in my lungs, there was a significant decrease in my liver and stomach and for the first time there was shrinkage in my spine. The grandness of the moment didn't escape me.

As I met with a few choice relatives and shared this good news, they seemed elated and happy to hear of my progress. Arguably they seemed more excited about my weight loss and how I looked. It's a strange thing that despite knowing everything I had gone through—the physical part meant more than the emotional, spiritual and even medical parts. I was taken aback by the shallowness of their understanding and sheer vanity. I was glad that I was living without mirrors and scales. Perhaps with them, I may not have focused so hard on what really matters—not just losing physical weight but everything else I had been carrying for so long.

On my return to Haasilgaon, further energized and willing to continue the routine, I started feeling for the first time that perhaps I did have a future. Perhaps this medicine, this life, this chance I had been given again was for the long haul. I had stopped planning for the future given that I didn't know what or how much lay ahead. But now with back-to-back scans showing marked improvements, it felt like it was time to start thinking, what next.

However I had time. Over the winter I stayed true to my routine, not letting any news get to me. Of course there were many events, engagements and celebrations during the time but it no longer felt like a first or something special, it was just a way of life. I had become a regular and the greatest feeling to develop was the feeling of belonging somewhere and knowing my purpose.

By the next scans, I was actually looking forward to my trip and it too proved successful as the results showed further marked improvements in my liver and stomach and my spine was stable.

As I made my way back to the village this time, I had celebrated my one-year anniversary in India. It was surprising how quickly time flew by but when I looked back and saw how much had actually transpired, it genuinely felt much longer.

With improved health and now a fixed routine, there were some practical issues that I needed to start focusing on again. One such issue was my visa and given the time away from the US, I was now going to need to make plans to manage everything that I had left behind. Three weeks had become a year and with my health only improving, there was no way I was going to go back to America now until I was without active cancer in my system.

I spoke to Mohanlalji about everything and he agreed that it was important for me to sort things out. He suggested I make the trip to Delhi and Mumbai and then come back and start a proper life there in Haasilgaon I was appreciative of his willingness to help me set up a life there, but I also knew my abilities and skills were professionally better matched for a big city.

In addition there was a thought that had lingered with me since my last trip to Mumbai. Was I ready to accept and embrace the simple life forever? At some point, I would need to return to my life, would I then be able to adjust? Would my health be able to manage that life?

I wasn't quite sure what the future had in store but I was extremely confident about one thing—my routine was not going to change—it would go with me wherever I went.

And off I went to Delhi.

Returning to the Shahs, more than a year after I had come to India, had a very full circle feel to it. They of course could barely recognize me, but the joy that I saw in all of them, really brought home to me what an adventure I had been on and how much difference a year could truly make.

As I navigated the urban world again, I missed the village more than anything. It seemed every conversation would end with me mentioning Sakhshi or the boys. Out of respect, I decided to visit Vinod Mama and Saroj Mami, to share with them my improved health. While they too were happy to see me fit and improved (after first not recognizing me), it felt like so much time had passed that the connection I had once felt was simply gone.

I managed to stay with Vinod Mama and Saroj Mami at their temple again. This time I wanted to stay because I had a home waiting for me back in Haasilgaon and I thought it would be worth it to get some face-to-face time with the many *sadhus* that were staying there at that time.

Two such lady *sadhus* I met, Sadhvi Nutan and Sadhvi Kiran Maharaj seemed to be there just to meet me. I had gone up with Saroj Mami who briefly introduced me to them. After she left, we continued to speak for hours. I had no idea that they generally only spoke once a week, on Sundays to devotees, but I became an exception. What should have been a one night stay turned into a week as I shared my life, my grief, my evolution, all of it with them.

It was the first time that I connected with my Jain religion. Sadhvi Nutan communicating in fluent English was the biggest bonus as she was able to explain to me things I otherwise simply couldn't understand.

But these women were not the typical *sadhus*. They were educated and rather than spending their time grooming other *sadhus*, they wrote books and determined that to be their legacy. As she explained she chose to become a doctor of the soul.

While our paths varied beyond belief, there were many similarities we shared. We had both left our families behind, shed ourselves of the many worldly things that otherwise consumed us. We both ate the same foods at the same time and lived a simple life, trying to do everything to achieve a greater connection to the land, the world and ultimately to our souls. We both walked barefoot (in my case ran barefoot), hoping to preserve all lives that inhabited the world, doing our best to keep things in balance.

They shared my journey with the many visiting *sadhus* one evening. It was clear that for them, what I had endured and how I was living seemed as if I had embraced their life, and in many ways far exceeded what they were doing. I had never thought of myself as a *sadhu* but it was the first time I realized how much I had transformed not just physically but spiritually as well.

I wanted to share this incredible experience with Monali. It had been many days since I had received a WhatsApp forward from her. She was always texting me messages of hope so her silence was a bad sign. Not able to reach her, I worried but felt confident that I'd hear back from her soon, with details in hand about a new therapy she just 'had' to try.

The week went by so quickly. I was overwhelmed by the questions I felt the need to answer. But I wasn't going to get them at Vinod Mama's place. Just as it happened, their daughter Radhika had come to visit Sadhvi Nutan and Sadhvi Kiran. She was surprised to see me there but very happy to meet me. Radhika and I had spent a lot of time together as kids and had reconnected when I returned to India. She was one of the few people to actually not just stay in touch but actually communicate something back to me while I was updating the family through regular e-mails while Mom was sick.

She had been drawn to my writing and my ability to express things. She too had followed her mother's footsteps and was making strides on her spiritual journey. While Saroj Mami was centered on religion—Radhika was focusing more on practicality and how religion could help on the road to spirituality. As I got to spend time with her, I realized that she had a larger following than even Saroj Mami.

She lived a rather reclusive life but wished to invite me into her private world. As I was sitting with her parents, I decided to accept since they were also insisting. I ended up staying a few days with her family and the larger Mission community that they had built their lives around. It was refreshing to see a group so devoted to the common purpose of bringing people together in finding their path. I was probably the right 'wandering soul' that could benefit from some time with them.

As it turned out, Radhika and I developed a bond of sharing our journeys. It was a special moment for me to have that connection with someone whom I called family. She had been absent from the disconnect and hurt because we were not in touch. I felt loved and respected, it was a welcome change. Perhaps I got attached so quickly that I felt comfortable sharing my vulnerabilities, given that I was at crossroads—contemplating my future.

I had spent some time with the Shahs, working with their daughter Kaira who had been setting up her own company. She wanted me to help her develop her brand and set up a website. Given our history and her being so instrumental in my coming to India—I felt like I needed to help, it wasn't an obligation but it was something I wanted to do. In a few weeks, she reminded me again of my talents, my capabilities and what I could offer the world. It was for the first time in years that I felt some worth. I had promised to deliver certain results for her and I managed to do that. There was no financial exchange but the longer I stayed there, the more I realized that whereas I was getting fulfilment, I was also going overboard. While my routine didn't suffer, my emotional investment coupled with my passion was blinding me from the reality, that I didn't need to do this and I actually still needed to concentrate on myself.

Radhika tried to decipher what had transpired to help, but it soon became clear to me that I was no longer an equal to her but rather I was becoming a student to her *'Prabhu'* status. I wasn't sure I could ever see her in that manner. We had a different relationship and given my history with Saroj Mami—I still had a long way to go in terms of trusting anyone without thinking there was an agenda. I wanted to trust but I couldn't muster the same leap of faith with Radhika as I had with the cows.

As I had to make my way to Mumbai to get my scans done—I wondered how I had let my life take such a detour. While I didn't have regrets, I felt without focus. In Haasilgaon, I had purpose. I began immersing myself with my previous world. It didn't feel like the one I had left behind. However I knew where I belonged—but I wasn't sure it was going to be practical.

CHAPTER 22

Alone In The Light

Even if your hands are shaking
And your faith is broken
Even as the eyes are closing
Do it with a heart wide open
Say what you need to say
['Say' by John Mayer]

My return to Mumbai was meant to be like every other trip, get my scans done and then head back to the village. However the reality of my situation had come to fruition with my decision to not return back to America—I did need to think about my financial future.

When the results showed significant improvement in my liver and stomach, I was relieved that my Delhi detour had not deterred my progress. I had been very careful to keep as much of my routine going and while Delhi was a bit of a challenge, Mumbai proved to be much easier.

Thanks to Neelam's family, they were able to find me a place in central Mumbai where I could stay on my own and still be near Meena Chachi and Sapna Massi, even though I wasn't counting on them for anything.

Thanks to its central location and easy walking distance to the local train, I was able to move around quite easily. Mumbai had a special option that I was told about and simply couldn't believe. Every local train had two compartments specifically delegated for handicapped and cancer patients.

I had not taken the local train since I was kid. Even then I remember how challenging it was to get on and off at any platform. But thanks to this bogie, I was once again able to move around freely without being stuck in never-ending traffic. It also permitted me the freedom to explore the city and find places that would accommodate my newly developed lifestyle.

Being an early riser, I thought the best place to breathe would be near the sea. My many scan trips to Mumbai had taught me how to get around and I was most familiar in Southern Mumbai. I had seen many people sit along the Queen's Necklace and look at the water.

I woke up at my usual time and hopped on to the first train towards town. It was a sight to be seen to have the entire compartment to myself. As no one was there, I realized that I could do my stretches and started to do certain yoga poses. In thirty five minutes I reached Churchgate station. Rather than walk my way to the sea, I began to run. I made it almost halfway home when I realized how far I had come. I decided to keep pushing myself and ran the rest of the way back. In all it was about 21 kms and gave me a thrilling rush as I realized that I had done a half-marathon. I immediately knew this was going to be a part of my morning routine while staying in Mumbai.

Near my room, I found an ashram that was associated with a neighbouring temple. They had several *desi* cows and once I informed them that I was a patient, they readily agreed to offer me the *gaumutra* and milk, daily. It was a relief, I knew to continue the treatment as my health improved, was important. While it may not have been as 'shubdh' as what I was consuming in the village, it was a saving grace.

211

Now that I knew my routine was set, I needed to focus on opportunities. Knowing that I had a home somewhere and a community still willing to be there for me provided such a safety net. I may have been living out of Haasilgaon but Haasilgaon was now inside of me.

While my time in Delhi had jumpstarted my creative juices it didn't necessarily live up to my expectations. I knew Mumbai would be the only place that could perhaps lead to something substantial.

Within a rather short time, I managed to secure some freelance work thanks to my contacts from the past. As luck would have it, my first night roommate from the hospital, Sarangee and I had stayed in touch over the last year. It seemed almost too coincidental that she worked in the development area of a film studio and I had previously dabbled in screenwriting. Over the course of the year in the village, I had also attempted to sell some of my completed scripts. Unfortunately, I was so focused on my health that I had lost out on a few opportunities, but my priorities were bang-on for the time frame.

However now my needs were different. I met her and almost immediately met with the creative team at the film studio, where they got to know about my history and also wished to know me as a writer. In a rather short while, I was given the task to write the treatment for a French film, that they had hoped to develop internally under the parent studio label.

I was told that this would be my test and if they liked my writing and style, they'd have me meet the additional creative executives and so on. In all my years of living in Los Angeles and being part of the industry, I did find it strange that there was no compensatory element in doing the work that I was asked to do, but I accepted this as the way things were run in India.

I wrote the French treatment followed by another one for a Korean film that they had also hoped to develop internally. After drafting two to three different versions, I was expecting some form of response but instead I got a call for another project, this time for the remake of a South Indian film that they wished to adapt into a Bollywood mainstream movie with an International action feel. While it was out of my comfort zone, my contact at the studio told me that this project was a priority as it would be with a very well respected and big production house and they would be overseeing the development.

I met with the producer and he gave me a general overview of his vision. In turn I submitted a version that he found too generic and with not enough 'masala'. I had suggested two options (one set in an International setting and one set in a local Indian setting). He agreed and I ended up writing two lengthier versions—far beyond what normally would be expected for such an assignment.

And then I waited. And I waited. And I waited. At the same time I realized that it had been far too long since I had heard from Monali. After making an incessant amount of calls to her number, someone finally answered the phone. Her husband regretfully informed me that she had passed away as a result of complications from her chemotherapy. I was devastated. I had wanted to share with her how my journey was continuing to unfold in the most dramatic of ways but she had found a way to upstage me.

As running had become my active meditative therapy, I used the open road to make some sense of this incredible loss. Why was I still standing and this wonderful young vibrant woman with a lovely family taken away so soon? She had tried every therapy with such positive energy—why was it her time to go? The questions seemingly took a backseat as I happened to pass by the coffee shop in Khar where all my film meetings were held. I saw the executive team with another team discussing the same movie—all the while I had never heard from them as to whether or not I was still in contention. I reviewed my calendar and realized that this process had already eaten up over four months of my time. My savings had further dwindled in anticipation of nothing.

Perhaps, I should have taken those months of work as a lesson that the expectation in India is to do the work and then wait for payment, if you are lucky—you'll get compensated. When you are trying so hard and being constantly tested, it's a tough pill to swallow and realize, that returning to the real world means having to deal with people taking advantage of you, having absolute disregard for your health and complete apathy for making use of your time and ideas for their own selfish advantage.

I had spent so much time avoiding the 'poison', it seemed that even with the ease of finding work, it was going to be a struggle to find purpose while assimilating back into the real world. Having just mourned the loss of Monali, I knew that I needed to find stability, happiness and more than anything else, a reason to justify my extended life.

It was a pleasant surprise then, to reconnect with Keyur, a friend of mine from High School. It felt great to be back in touch with someone who knew where I had come from and how far I had come. Minus an interested family, I seldom had reminders in my day-to-day life of my past and the person that I used to be.

Perhaps the attachment that I have for the past got me overexcited at the prospect of working with him, when the opportunity arose, in his company. Without much thought on either of our sides, we agreed to work together. I had some restrictions as a result of my visa status in India but was assured that things could be sorted and so I began to work.

For the first time since coming to India, I thought I was going to have the chance to perhaps settle into a job, restore my level of financial security and actually have a routine that enabled me to manage my health and build a life again.

The work was fulfilling enough and my relationship with colleagues blossomed. Yet as each workday progressed, I realized that the complexities of working fulltime again plus maintaining my health, was a challenge beyond my expectation. There was a sense of relief that I'd soon settle into my own flat and have the space and the luxury to afford support for my day-to-day tasks.

Unfortunately or perhaps fortunately, with each passing day I realized that being compensated and getting my own place was not going to happen as easily as I had initially thought. In fact, any form of payment without changing my visa status was most likely impossible.

I understood the legal issues and tried to work to have things resolved as swiftly as possible. However the reality of the situation was that in India nothing moves as quickly as we want. In addition, yet again, I found myself at the mercy of others. As I looked at the calendar again, almost six months had passed since leaving Haasilgaon. I was delving further into my savings in anticipation of work.

Despite all my efforts and these amazing opportunities, when the time came for getting paid, I had nothing to show for it. I thought about how this had happened. At any other point in my life I would have been bitter. I would have fought back or not permitted situations to end in the manner they did. What had changed?

India may have saved me but in the course of a few months, trying to live here and become a contributing member of society again, proved to not only be a continued exercise in patience but a test for my willingness to accept anything at any cost.

I had a choice to make, whether to accept this life and these circumstances. But I couldn't come this far and jeopardize my health again. Would it make sense to reassimilate myself simply to prove that I had 'made it' back from the verge?

On one side I thought I wanted to recapture the life that had once consumed me, but on the other was my ability to now live under any condition anywhere and find happiness there. Given that context, I knew that city life was perhaps not what I was cut out for anymore. The pace of life, the lack of value for people and their health and the complete disregard for one's happiness left me feeling more alone than I had felt in a long while.

As I started to question again if there really was any choice left, I had another set of scans. With the added stressors of Delhi and Mumbai life, I wasn't sure that the improvements were going to show. I may have maintained my routine, but mentally, I was in a very different zone. The scans proved me wrong yet again. They showed no detection of cancer in my liver and significant shrinkage in my stomach and spine. I was in a state of disbelief, that despite my modified lifestyle, I was thriving physically.

Mumbai was good for my physical health and it also permitted me to have a social life—but I needed a purpose. And not just the free work I was handing out to people who were in no need of charity and were profiting while I myself was struggling. But there was solace—a silver lining if you will. Despite all these headaches, I managed to find time to speak with other patients and caregivers. Whether we met on the local train or they heard about me through word of mouth, I was developing a network, similar to the one at the hospital, but much more global as it turned out.

I was more than happy to share what I had learnt and the good will I got in return was no match. Perhaps these blessings are what kept me going, the faith they had in me helped to ward off any of the stress that work and its complications were causing. But everyone has a breaking point and while I had so many mechanisms in place to handle any challenge—my body was beginning to tell another story.

Had I not known the signs, I'm sure I would not have been as lucky as I was that early Monday morning. It was ironic that the mini-stroke I had, was happening on the day I was supposed to officially leave my job to prepare for my departure from Mumbai and head back to Haasilgaon.

What happened in turn was quite possibly the most horrifying chapter of my recent medical life. The most terrible part about the proceeding days, as I recovered and fought a nasty viral infection, was that in reality; despite my attempts to feel settled and at ease in Mumbai over so many months, I ultimately had very few people by my side.

I had already accepted the lack of involvement from any blood relations but living in Mumbai and seeing friends who had known me for only a few months, step in and offer their time, their space, their money and even their love unlike the people that could so easily offer this but chose not to, was humbling. Yet again, the reminder that

217

the kindness of strangers was guiding me couldn't be stronger.

As my workplace found out about my health, it was an interesting moment. There was concern but in a way there seemed to be relief too. In any other job I was used to having visits from employers, flowers and get well soon messages. Here instead, I saw that my work email was immediately shut down. My first email from the company requested that my work laptop be picked up, no mention of anything else. It was strange to see such absurd behaviour from professionals who were also supposedly my friends. But friendship is something that requires care and concern and a level of selflessness, something that waited for me back in Haasilgaon.

I felt lucky but at the same moment, for the first time since leaving the hospital for the second instance, I felt like a burden. I had promised myself never to be in that position yet somehow this had happened again.

I needed to move on in my gypsy life alone, but with the support of an amazing tribe.

CHAPTER 23

Let Go, Let Up & Live For Today

Umeed bandh ho gaya tha
Par ek Maa ne phir se jageya
Yeh to sach hai ke maine socha
Zindagi mein kuch aur nahin tha

Par tune to jadoo kiya hai
Is sharir pe Maa
Phir se chalne lage hain hum
Sirf tujhse Maa

Gaumata Gaumata Gaumata Ki Jai
Sab Ke Rakhwale Gaumata hamare
O Gaumata Gaumata Gaumata Ki Jai
Sab Ke Rakhwale Gaumata hamare

['Gaumata Ki Jai' by Amit Vaidya]

Letting go is a daily process. As much as we say it's easy to let go, it's not. It's not easy because there are daily reminders of what is and isn't, who is and who isn't. But the world is not as negative as we presume. We just have to seek out that positivity—wherever it is.

I realized this a long time ago but struggled with applying it. I would find the positivity and internalize it but I'd also try to be an ear, a saviour of sorts for negativity. Interacting with people who live in misery and being there as a positive light is a service, but it can also be very draining.

Living the urban life in Mumbai, I couldn't help but see how many people had forgotten what happiness is. Everyone

219

lived in a constant state of stress and it became infectious for me. My mini-stroke was ultimately a victim of this intolerable cruelty that the modern world has now accepted as the norm.

But as I sat on my friend's bed recovering, I realized that my life, my world, having gone through so much, it couldn't be just for this. Perhaps I needed to prove to myself and perhaps also to the outside world (which ultimately I said I didn't care for, but in reality a big part of me still did), that I could comeback from my deathbed and make my mark again in society.

But in the process of doing this, I lost myself. I lost the person who had left the world that he knew and decided to try anything to live, survive and build a new healthy happy life for himself.

I realized that perhaps, now the non-city life was truly my home, the only person I needed to satisfy was myself and the best way to do that was to serve others. After having let go of so much—my name, my work, my family, my relatives, my money, my identity—I was restarting but I was making the same mistakes I had previously made, all over again.

Sure I was taking care of my health, going for runs, taking my medicine, but the discipline and schedule remained ineffective if I was not in the right state of mind. I had accepted that my limitations were now decreasing but as I assimilated back into the 'real' world—I was forsaking my happiness for conditioned pleasure.

With that I realized that my life was never going to 'go back to the same'. We all have a purpose in life. Sometimes life changes our priorities and my life now wasn't meant to be sitting in an office and working for a pay check that would provide me luxury and comfort. The only real thing I needed (I guess always) was love.

I never felt short changed when my parents were alive. I managed to feel that security somewhat continue while in America, till I came to India. Those first few weeks in India, I felt rejuvenated with the physical presence of my extended family and relatives. But then I decided to stay in India and just as quickly I saw that disappear.

What I was left with was the love of my parents from above, the support of my friends from so far away and a life now defined by the kindness of strangers. For over two years now, my life has continued to be based on those, who have selflessly taken to being there for me in whatever fashion it was needed.

I feel so blessed to have had so many angels guide me along these last two years. Giving me the encouragement to actually recover, reminding me that I can still give something back to society and I'm not just some washout who has lived past his expected terminal date of death.

If there is one regret that still haunts me, it is the mistake I made in the hospital in New York over eight years ago, when I was told that I had cancer. I heard the doctor tell me that I'd be fine and that 'we'll beat this'.

Today, I look back and think how naïve I was in believing him. Perhaps there was truth in what he said but like everything else in our life—why must we define it by an end date. Life isn't about beating cancer it is about living with cancer.

For eight years and counting, I've been living with cancer. I wish I believed that I could live and manage this disease. While my life is still determined by quarterly scans and I'm only as healthy as my last scan—my happiness is constant.

221

For a long time, the guilt of not being able to repay the support that my friends and family gave me, fuelled my illness. However part of letting go was realizing that sometimes for your own survival, you have to do things you'd never thought you'd have to, want to or even need to—but then again, the judgment we bear comes from above and not from inside.

To this day, I wonder why we are so quick to give up on people. Perhaps time, our own insecurities or simply our own selfish desires dictate how we behave in the modern world. If there is anything I wish to pass on to the world it is that rather than disappearing, not pursuing or expecting the patient to stay in touch and update you—if you are actually concerned—find ways to not just be inspired by them but find ways to inspire them.

The notion that I came to India in search of a final farewell and to now know it was possible to reach cancer-free status, after everything that had happened— it is nothing short of a miracle. But I worked hard. I held on to faith even when it was so much easier to give up. I didn't take one moment, one day for granted. I needed to believe that each day I lived with or without cancer now, I was well into my second life. I shouldn't be here, but I'm here for a reason. And with that, I have absolutely no plans to change my life, my routine, my day-to-day way of being. It is simply not worth the risk—but more importantly it's who I am now. After all, everything that turned around with my new life, it was all put in place not just to cure me but to also improve my life, and now that I've benefited from the bonus portion—the maintenance of the cancer—I refuse to let an improved prognosis stop me from what is now my way of life.

While there are certainly no guarantees for the future, I am very sure of one thing. Today, I've beat cancer and found a way to live my life to the fullest and healthiest—something I never thought would have been possible two, four, six or even eight years ago. All the wishful thinking in the world wouldn't have saved me if I didn't have discipline, a routine and faith. Faith in myself, my Earth and fellow human beings—strangers who let me live, survive and thrive.

We often ignore the costs associated with the risks we take. The financial costs of my treatment and healing in India, over the span of two years, equalled perhaps not even two month's cost of my time in the United States. The added weight we associate with the price of things directly relating to quality and remedy—is false. In this journey of truly returning to simplicity, I now understand why the best things in life are closer to free.

I look back now and wonder what really got me started. Was it frankly as simple as not having a choice? Was it that I was trying to cling on to life so hard that I was willing to do anything? Was it the faith I had instilled in myself that despite the loss of both of my parents and the full absence of my extended family—I needed to prove I could live? Or was it just that I had always smiled, laughed and endured no matter what and with the prospect of having more surprises (both the welcome and unwelcome kind)—I decided it was better to try than to just wait to die.

I've always gone to sleep in peace no matter where, no matter when. My eyes open like clockwork at 4:27 am. I get up, pray and drink my morning's first glass of water. I wonder each day what life has in store for me on that day. As I start my routine, I always say my *Navkar Mantra* and feel so grateful to have another day. It's all that we have in our control—for we have no control of the next moment so each moment, we must live it, we must live for today.

I left Mumbai without looking back. The minute I let life guide me again rather than dictating the rules myself—my world opened that much further. Every voice became a voice ready and willing to help and to let me be who I had now become. I was back to my organic life. I travelled to Delhi with the goal to head towards the foothills of the Himalayas—to recoup, write and reflect on everything that had transpired.

As a reminder of everything that had just consumed me, I reunited with some old high school friends. It was a wonderful evening. As we chronicled the night with photographs, I noticed that my smile was crooked. It seems somewhere along the trainride from Mumbai to Delhi, I was gifted with Bell's palsy as a result of the nerve damage from my mini-stroke. It felt like it was the final test that I needed to pass. Could I still be happy without showing the smile that I had so constantly photographed myself with, carrying on no matter where I was, how I was living or with whom.

As I left Delhi and headed to my next destination Naukuchiatal, I realized that now even my face would no longer be able to dictate my feelings. I needed to simply express them and let my life guide me rather than any impressions someone would get on first contact. Upon reaching my new home, for the moment two things were clear—I still had a lot of healing to do and that I was destined to give back and heal myself by healing others.

A disease, a smile, our words or our relations cannot define us—we are defined by what stays with us—our memories. It's the only thing we should pack when traveling. It fits in even the smallest of bags and frankly it's the only real thing of value we carry. Everything else is temporary. Realizing this simple truth is the final act in truly letting go. Embracing this reality no matter how bleak, allows you to accept each moment, each chapter—as a gift.

As Mom's speech quickly degenerated at the end of her life, she latched onto a few choice words. 'Please', 'thank you' and 'love you' were staples but it was two phrases she repeated to almost anyone who would listen. One was 'live for today'. It's something I've tried to follow every single day since the day she's died. The other was that 'every day is perfect'—that's something I feel truly blessed to now embody.

In July 2014, I reached a milestone. I had a feeling that was long gestating in my body but I was afraid to actually hear the words. As I sat under that very familiar white light again, I was fearful because after having finally accepted a life and a lifestyle... to hear the words 'cancer-free'—it felt overwhelming and unreal. So much contributed to my recovery yet I feel so much work is still to be done.

From 'holy shit' to 'holy cow'—I have been blessed because of this holy cancer.

Touchdown

I'm alive because of faith, routine, discipline, humanity, money, chemotherapy, cow therapy, radiation, friends, family, strangers, villages, cows... the list is endless.

No one thing is responsible for keeping me alive.

A cow 'saved' me but she wasn't the sole 'cure'.

Allopathy and Ayuveda need to work together.

Hope is the staple garnish we must use as seasoning for practicality.

People are people throughout the world—no one place is better or worse.

We ultimately let an environment place its importance (whether positive or negative) in our lives.

I'm only as healthy as my last scan.

This is all bonus time and I'm never going to forget that fact.

I'm prepared if the cancer returns and I'll accept whatever comes my way.

In life, the only guarantee we have is our death.

Be the best advocate you can be for yourself.

Never laugh or think that an opinion offered (a real opinion, not a judgment) is not worth pursuing until you've scoped out its merits.

We are capable of far more than we think and we are able to endure far more that we give ourselves credit for.

Don't think luxury means longevity.

Sometimes the less we have, the more we get.

Stop asking the why and start answering with why not.

Every question does not have an answer.

But there is an answer for every question even if we don't ask it.

Navkar Mantra

Namo Arihantanam
I bow down to Arihanta
Namo Siddhanam
I bow down to Siddha
Namo Ayariyanam
I bow down to Acharya
Namo Uvajjhayanam
I bow down to Upadhyaya
Namo Loe Savva-sahunam
I bow down to Sadhu and Sadhvi
Eso Panch Namokaro
These five bowings downs
Savva-pavappanasano
Destroy all the sins
Manglananch Savvesim
Amongst all that is auspicious
Padhamam Havei Mangalam
This Navkar Mantra is the foremost

The cows that saved my life

The hospital at Sevak

My room

My first day of Gaumutra
& Panchgavya

With Monali & Rajeev,
My cancer brother & sister

My hospital family

@ the hospital Gaushala

Feeding our way to blessings

Nothing more special or sacred

Serenity in numbers

Newborn calf and I drinking the same milk

The farm

My home in Haasilgaon

My room

Our water reservoir

A 'moo' away from the Gaushala

The godam next to my room

Ganga – "my saviour"

Sakshi – "my soulmate"

Pomegranates & Bananas @ the farm

Grapes, Sugarcane & Turmeric @ the farm

15th August/Indepedence Day Celebrations
at Haasilgaon

Life on the Farm

Team AV America: The Village Boys

Contemplating Next Steps...

...Accepting What Is

Sakshi & Me

Gaumata Ki Jai

Umeed bandh ho gaya tha
I had closed all expectations
Phir ek Maa ne phir se jagaya
Then one mother woke them up
Yeh to sach hai ke maine socha
It's true that I thought
Zindagi mein kuch aur nahin tha
There was nothing left in life
Par tune to jadoo kiya is sharir pe Maa
But you did magic on this body Mother
Phir se chalne lage hain hum, sirf tujhse o Maa
I've started to walk again, only because of you Mother

Gaumata Gaumata Gaumata ki Jai
Hail victory to Mother Cow
Sab ke rakhewale Gaumata hamare
She protects all of us, that's our Mother Cow
Gaumata Gaumata Gaumata ki Jai
Hail victory to Mother Cow
Sab ke rakhewale Gaumata hamare
She protects all of us, that's our Mother Cow

Roz roz dekh ke chain aa gaya
Seeing you everyday gave me peace
Gaushala mein jaake, darshan mil gaya
Going to the Gaushala we got your blessings
Karenge roz hum aapka seva
We're going to care for you everyday
Na bhulenge ab hum tumhara chehra
And we'll never forget your face
Par tune to shanti diya hai is mann ko Maa
But you gave peace to this mind Mother
Phir se jeene lage hain hum, sirf tujhse o Maa
I've started to live again, only because of you Mother

Gaumata Gaumata Gaumata ki Jai
Hail victory to Mother Cow
Sab ke rakhewale Gaumata hamare
She protects all of us, that's our Mother Cow
Gaumata Gaumata Gaumata ki Jai
Hail victory to Mother Cow
Sab ke rakhewale Gaumata hamare
She protects all of us, that's our Mother Cow

Glossary

Aarti: a Hindu ceremony in which lights with wicks are soaked in ghee are then lit and offered up to deities

Apasra: the space that houses Shwetambar/Sthanakwasi Jain Maharajis

Asanas: specific yoga poses

Babaji: a spiritual or religious dignitary generally with some special power/ability

Bahut: a lot/quite a bit

Bhabhi: brother's wife

Bhai: brother

Bhajans: a devotional song

Bhole O Bhole: a song title from the film "Yaarana" — the song calls out to Lord Shiva

Chachi: father's brother's wife

Chai: Indian-spiced black tea

Chauviar: no food or water between sunset and the next morning sunrise. Many Jains practice this daily

Desi: pure Indian

Dhaba: a roadside restaurant

Dhol: a type of drum

Dhyan: meditation

Didi: sister

Gaumata: Mother Cow

Gaumutra: the urine from Mother Cow

Gaushala: the area where the Mother Cow resides

Ghee: clarified butter of Mother Cow

Gobar: dung of Mother Cow

Guruji: a spiritual or religious dignitary generally with many devotees

Hijra: a eunuch

Ho jayega: a common phrase to say that something 'will get done'

Hum Saath Saath Hain: a film from 1999—literal translation 'We Are All Together'

Jai Gurudev: the greeting recited by followers of Sri Sri Ravi Shankar

Jhuggi: a slum dwelling usually made of mud

Jowar: sorghum

Kaddu: pumpkin

Kal Ho Na Ho: a film from 2003 — literal translation 'There May Or May Not Be A Tomorrow'

Kala: dark or black

Kanda bhajji: onion fritters

Karela: bitter gourd

Kitna tasty khana hai na: 'the food is very tasty'

Kunjal-kriya: a yoga cleansing technique

Kurta pajama: a lengthy tunic and loose pants generally worn by men

Lasoon: garlic

Lauki: bottle gourd

Maharajis: saints or religious monks. In Jainism, these 'sadhus' are also referred to as Maharajis

Mama: mother's brother

Mami: mother's brother's wife

Mandir: temple

Mantra: a prayer or the word/line recited repeatedly during meditation.

Massa: mother's sister's husband

Massi: mother's sister

Mattu Pongal: Indian holiday celebrating the first day of harvests

Mere Desh Ki Dharti: song title from the film Upkar. A very popular patriotic song of India.

Methi: fenugreek

Mudra: yoga poses

Murti-puja: praying to a statued diety

Nani: mother's mother

Navkar Mantra: the first prayer recited by Jains

Neem: Azadirachta indica

Om ka Jaap: a repeated 'mantra' concentrating on the word 'Om'

Palak: spinach

Pan wala: vendor making mouth fresheners

Panchgavya: a drink composed of desi cow milk, ghee, curd, gaumutra and gobar

Panchkarma: an Ayurvedic detoxification treatment involving massage and other herbal therapies

Parvel: pointed gourd

Poha: generally a breakfast dish made with flattened rice

Prabhu: master or lord

Pranayama: in yoga, the exercises that focus primarily on breathing

Pravachan: a sermon, religious lecture

Roti: an Indian flatbread generally made of whole wheat flour

Saas-bahu: a reference to the numerous television soap operas that focus on the at-home conflict between mother-in-laws and daughter-in-laws

Sabha: townhall meeting place

Sadhu: a saint or religious leader

Salwar kameez: a long tunic and pants worn by women

Shubdh: pure

Surya Namaskar: a specific yoga pose generally to be
    performed at sunrise bowing down to the sun as she
    rises

Thali: a fixed dish comprising of roti, dal, vegetables and rice

Tulsi: holy basil

Tutta-futta: 'broken'

Ukala: an herbal drink heated with various leaves, spices
    and seasonings

Upma: a breakfast dish generally made with semolina flour

HEALING
VAIDYA

My road to recovery has been as much a journey of uncovering the beauty of the world as it has been about self-discovery.

In the time that has followed since I set off to write this book, I've met such amazing individuals who've guided me along an organic path of sharing knowledge and becoming a fulltime medical advocate. The joy that I've had spending time with countless patients throughout India is a gift I wouldn't return for any price.

The most special part of this reward has been the confidence it has bestowed on me to recognize that I am actually making a difference. And thanks to the many who've become friends along this process, my message of inspiration and each person becoming their own best advocate for all matters of health and wellbeing has begun to spread.

This has directly led to the creation of **Healing Vaidya**, a NGO providing a scaled platform to expand on this very message and provide alternative avenues in wellness.

As a result Healing Vaidya will focus on publishing— building bridges between individuals and information thereby creating a balance in dialogue and decision-making.

Beyond this book, we will be distributing diet cheat-sheets to patients at hospitals free of charge. Patients deserve the right to know what will aid them in their recovery and taking that one step further, what may prevent the illness in the first place. We will also be creating a series of healthy cookbooks incorporating the many healthy homemade recipies I've picked up or had shared with me along the journey. We will be creating an end-of-life forum that provides families with support when time comes to make decisions for palliative care. We will also create a wellness blog guiding individuals about incorporating wellness into their daily health routine. And finally, I will continue to work actively with families and patients to ensure that no one ever feels they don't have an option or that the lack of knowledge has stopped them from trying something they wanted.

Healing Vaidya's sole mission is to educate, inspire and empower every person to find the right healing path for themselves to ensure that they are living each day with happiness as the constant.

It would be my greatest honour to have your support with this mission.

If you would like to contribute to Healing Vaidya, donations are kindly accepted.

Please visit our website www.healingvaidya.org for details on how to contribute.